The Scientific Conscience

The Scientific Conscience

*Reflections on the Modern
Biologist and Humanism*

CATHERINE ROBERTS

George Braziller
NEW YORK

Q
175
.R6

Acknowledgments

In the preparation of this book several persons have provided stimulating counsel and encouragement. Others have spent valuable time in furnishing practical aid. Some have done both. Those to whom I am particularly grateful are Richard Thorne, Charles Davy, Lewis Mumford, Basil Wrighton, and Lancelot Whyte.

C. R.

For permission to quote from copyright material, grateful acknowledgment is made:

To Oxford University Press for quotation from PAIDEIA by Werner Jaeger, and from THE RISE OF THE GREEK EPIC by Gilbert Murray.

To Harper & Row for quotation from LITERATURE AND SCIENCE by Aldous Huxley and from BRAVE NEW WORLD REVISITED by Aldous Huxley.

To Random House for quotation from THE IMMENSE JOURNEY by Loren Eiseley.

Preface

Each chapter of this book was conceived and written as an independent essay during the period 1961–1966 and follows in chronological order. Now, five years after the first one was begun, a brief, retrospective consideration of the original incentives for attempting this work may possibly serve to arouse the reader's interest in the pages to follow.

However much we may wish to the contrary, motives are never purely idealistic but always to some degree dependent upon the unavoidable interplay of intellectual and emotional idiosyncrasies with the external conditions of our existence. Yet I believe now that the two primary motives for beginning these essays, vague and tenuous as they were at the time, were, first, a need to enlarge my horizons and, second, a need to express my growing discontent with the mental outlook prevailing in that field of science which I knew best.

Nearly twenty years' experience as a professional microbiologist had naturally brought me into close contact with many American and European colleagues, and, like them, I had long felt that it was required of me to accept without question the conventional outlook of my profession. As time went on, however, such passive acceptance of the flowing tide of scientism brought me face to face with so many novel trends and ideas in biological research that some kind of questioning, if not protest, became inevitable. To ask, "What is the present mental outlook of the modern biologist?" thus appeared as no trivial inquiry answerable only by a trivial generalization, but rather as a necessary question to which an enlightening answer could be reasonably expected.

To begin with, it was necessary to assume that the scientist's outlook is derived from his sincere and lifelong devotion to science. This assumption is more than an expression of the obvious. It also signifies that a scientist's devotion to the attainment of new, objective truths about the world in order to understand, exploit, and transform it for the benefit of mankind must for him take precedence over all other forms of devotion. And it is true that in his capacity as a scientist, the modern biologist is primarily devoted to the acquisition of all new scientific facts that can elucidate the unsolved problems of the origin, maintenance, and development of life. Since this goal naturally includes all new facts about man, the outlook of the modern biologist, with its commitment to man's future progress, appears at first glance to be of the greatest human significance.

On second thought, the fact remains that whether or not the Two Cultures actually exist, there does lie outside the domain of science a realm of spiritual values that science denies. The moral philosophy, the art, the music, and the literature, which constitute most of the superior knowledge of our cultural heritage, have no place in the scientist's laboratory. Yet does not this realm of the human spirit contain more of the essence of life than even the biologists dream of? Is not the subjective world outlook derived from it more humanly significant than the objective world outlook of science? And if so, would it not be the height of folly to permit contemporary biologists to apply their scientific knowledge to control and direct the further development of human life?

A preliminary attempt to deal with such questions resulted in the essay, "The Modern Biologist at the Crossroads," the first chapter of this book. The remaining chapters are all expansions of this basic theme, comprising specific examples of the contemporary scientific outlook. While they could easily be multiplied, these few examples should be sufficient to persuade the reader of the desirability of reconsidering our ideas about the science of life.

In contrast to most writers of our day who pronounce critical judgment upon any aspect of the advance or application of modern science, I make no apologies for any anti-scientific or anti-progressive thoughts expressed herein. Actually, this book in its entirety represents a deliberate attack upon the conventional scientific outlook which now dominates world thought. The reader must not, however, expect to find in it any new facts, any novel contribution, or any hitherto unknown *Weltanschauung*. It is primarily an attempt by a scientifically educated person to orient her thinking about the role of biology in human evolution; and "orient," it should be stressed, according to Webster, means "to set right, by adjusting to principles." A more apposite word could scarcely be imagined. For the basic theme of these *Reflections on the Modern Biologist and Humanism* seems inherently "right" to me—not because of any personal experience or specific revelation, but because it is derived from spiritual principles, concepts, and values of the past which appear in every humanly significant way to transcend the mental climate of our times.

For this reason, I am advocating that our vision of man's future development take into account another outlook which is based upon a set of values as old as the hills—or, at least, as old as the Psalms. This proposal is made in full recognition of the fact that the greatest visions and ideals of the past are now generally dismissed as hopelessly antiquated for our modern world. How could it be otherwise, when the prevailing beliefs of our times are dominated by science? For science proclaims that evolutionary progress primarily depends upon the attainment of new knowledge through the unlimited expansion of the human intellect. Whether the alternative outlook advocated here will evoke any sympathetic response in our Scientific Age depends upon whether I have been able to convince the reader that the twentieth century's faith in the unrestricted advance of modern biology can be challenged with both heart and mind.

C. R.

Holte, Denmark

Contents

The Scientific Conscience

I

The Modern Biologist
at the Crossroads

*For not to know, either awake or in a dream, the nature
of justice and injustice, and good and evil, cannot in truth
be otherwise than disgraceful to him, even though he
have the applause of the whole world.*
—Plato, Phaedrus, 277e.

Present Trends in Biological Research

To scientists and laymen alike, international scientific congresses
can be awe-inspiring. Consider the thousands of assembled
participants, including the greatest names within the field, the
hundreds of scientific papers, the eventual voluminous publication of the congress proceedings, and the years of preparation
that efficient congress organization requires. This vast expendi-
ture of time, energy, and funds can only be undertaken because
the dissemination and discussion of new scientific information are
considered to be of vital importance in our modern world. The
success of these enormous enterprises can therefore be regarded
as a true sign of the times, symbolizing, as it does, the accelerating progress of Man the Scientist.

Let me try briefly to characterize him. Could it not be said, for
example, that the modern scientist is one who is engaged in the

most fashionable occupation of the twentieth century and who, in his insatiable thirst for knowledge, recognizes no boundaries or limitations to his activity? Here not only the most admirable quality of the scientist, his unceasing quest for truth is emphasized, but also the importance of social prestige, without which science could not flourish. In justifiable elation over our hitherto astounding successes in science, we feel that there is nothing, and shall be nothing, to stop us now. It is thus taken for granted that civilized society will always be interested in providing means to support scientific research and that the pursuit of science will necessarily continue at an ever-increasing tempo. It is this triumphant note, this spirit of elation, which permeates the scientific meeting of today; and it is just this atmosphere which also arouses foreboding.

In order to express more precisely this undercurrent of misgiving with respect to the future of biology, we must at the outset attempt to define its ultimate aim. For most biologists, the immediate goal is the discovery of new facts about life on this planet in the hope that such knowledge, in conjunction with accepted principles of mathematics, physics, and chemistry, will eventually establish new biological generalizations and provide a more complete understanding of the phenomenon of life. And the further we penetrate into the essential nature of life itself, the more successfully will biology be able to solve problems concerned with mastery of the environment, food supply, and medicine. Thus, in view of material benefit to mankind, modern society regards the accumulation of knowledge *per se* as an admirable justification for the continued activity of the biologist. We must, however, not stop with these prospects, for in its triumphant advance, biology is not content with understanding life, much less respecting it: now, with undiminished optimism and with apparent lack of recognition of the possible consequences, it desires to alter life.

In scores of biological laboratories throughout the world, bacteria, yeasts, and other microorganisms are being subjected to various physical and chemical treatments for the purpose of producing permanent and inheritable alterations in their genetic constitutions, and the mutant forms thus produced are then studied either directly or after having been subjected to crossing experiments. These investigations, which are by no means of recent date, have been of inestimable value to geneticists and biochemists alike in dealing with such problems as the determination of genes responsible for the expression of phenotypic characters, the location of the genes on the chromosomes, the relation of the genes to the synthesis of specific enzymes, enzymatic adaptation, the frequency of mutation, and the chemical basis of heredity. It should be noted that these induced mutations of the laboratory, like the spontaneous mutations occurring in nature, are random, unpredictable events; but of late the possibility of directed mutation—that is, the production at will of specific mutations in microorganisms by specific inducing agents—has attracted much attention.

Another field which has been extensively examined involves the genetic alteration of bacteria by the naturally occurring process of bacteriophage transduction or by artificially induced transformation. The results attained in this field have led to the concept of chemical hybridization, which could be of practical significance, since it may be possible to produce, by means that could never occur in nature, industrially important microorganisms with desirable specific characters. Briefly, this technique involves the extraction of a gene precursor (deoxyribonucleic acid, or DNA) from cells which possess the desired character, followed by its administration to cells lacking the character in the hope that they will thereby acquire it. Biochemical genetics does not, however, exclusively employ microorganisms as its test object. Of particular interest today is the use of animal tissue cultures in attempts to make genetic analyses of phenotypic differences at the cellular level. Human tissue cultures are also being employed for this purpose, and although the technical difficulties are at present great, successful results, of undoubted significance to medicine, have been predicted.

Possible Consequences of the Further Advance of Biology

No one can doubt that the wholehearted and enthusiastic support given to these modern trends in biology is based upon (1) the fact that science has hitherto played an enormously important role in the amelioration of human welfare, and (2) the honest belief that it will continue to do so. But at this stage in the history of mankind, a more critical attitude toward the possible consequences of the biologist's activity seems desirable.

It is no longer fanciful to suppose that in the near future the biologist—and here are included the geneticist, the microbiologist, and the biochemist—will be successful in his attempts to induce in microorganisms desired mutations at will and to produce chemical hybrids of a desired genotype; and, furthermore, that the genetic constitution of man will become susceptible of analysis. Without recourse to these possibilities, proposals have already been made for directing human evolution by the establishment of sperm and egg banks from rigorously selected individuals. It is obvious that when these various desiderata are attained, the genetic control of *Homo sapiens* is then feasible. It has been repeatedly seen in the history of science that only a short period need intervene between a scientific discovery and its practical application: already dimly emergent on the scientific horizon is the specter of a superman.

For those who are intoxicated by the precipitate advance of modern biology, the possibility of man being able by artificial genetic means to shape his own destiny is nothing less than a promise of a better world to come. I do not share this optimism. To state the case in its simplest terms: biology, just as nuclear physics before it, has now for the first time come face to face with moral values without recognizing its predicament. According to the recent views of one of the world's leading geneticists, the prospect of directed human evolution through artificial selection carries with it such great hopes for the future of mankind that its mere contemplation excites jubilation. In the nearly complete absence of critical opposition to this viewpoint, it must be assumed that the modern biologist (1) shares this optimism, (2) is uninterested, or (3) has no time to reflect upon the matter owing to his preoccupation with daily scientific problems. There are, however, some biologists today who have felt it necessary to point out that the limitation of scientific activity is at least worthy of consideration. In discussing man considered as an object of biology, Sirks has this to say:

[L'homme] sera forcé de reconnaitre que les rayons reflétés par son autoportrait, forment un spectre riche et varié, renfermant, à côté des rayons froids du violet, toute la gamme des couleurs jusqu'au rouge le plus chaud. . . . De côté du froid violet on trouvera l'intelligence, dans les raies plus chaudes des couleurs le tempérament, le caractère: maitrise de soi, responsabilité, énergie et émotionnalité. Nous approchons du domaine invisible des rayons infrarouges, les rayons de chaleur: altruïsme, amour du prochain, abnégation, les dons supérieurs dont peut disposer l'homme. C'est là que l'homme-humain devra former sa vision lui-même, c'est là que sa foi dominera sa compréhension. C'est là que le biologue, comme savant, croit devoir se taire. La parole cède au silence.[1]

([Man] will be forced to recognize that the rays of light reflected by his self-portrait form a rich and varied spectrum comprising the whole color scale from the cold violet rays to the warmest red. . . . At the cold violet end we find intelligence, in the warmer colors, temperament and character: self-control, responsibility, energy, and emotion. We approach the invisible realm of infrared, the rays of heat: altruism, love of one's neighbor, self-denial, the superior gifts which are available to man. This is where the human being must form his own vision; this is where his faith will dominate his understanding. This is where the biologist, as a scholar, recognizes that he cannot speak. Words yield to silence.)

To be sure, this complete withdrawal of man's spiritual characters from the sphere of genetics has no scientific foundation but is rather the personal belief of Sirks as well as of other geneticists; on the other hand, there are those who are confident that science will one day have something to say about the moral aspect of human behavior. With respect to the envisaged development of the science of human breeding, both points of view must be considered. If, on the one hand, we assume that spiritual characters will forever remain incapable of genetic analysis and control and that the preeminence of the contemplated superman can lie only in superior intelligence and physical well-being, then surely this project is doomed from the start by its utter neglect of the very essence of man's greatness—his soul. If, on the other hand, we assume that moral characters will eventually be brought under scientific control, we have no assurance whatever that this control will be exercised by morally superior individuals or corporate bodies.

Furthermore, we need not limit ourselves to spiritual characters; with respect to any controlled character desirable in man, how do the proponents of human breeding answer the question, "Desired by whom?" In other words, who is to choose what characters are "best," and on what basis are they to be chosen? The contemplation of scientists and governments, irresponsible or otherwise, having in their power the means of creating a future race of supermen is nothing less than appalling. The problem of controlled human breeding, in its immensity, may be compared to that of nuclear physics and atomic weapons; here the attitude of many scientists implies that it is regrettable that man's moral concepts have not kept pace with his scientific and technological advances, but, notwithstanding, this is truly a "great age for science" and no obstacles to its progress can be permitted. Only recently an appeal was made in America to double the national support for science, the annual requirements being specified as 1.5 billion dollars.[2] A better alternative might be for biologists to begin to reflect upon the direction in which they are heading and to become cognizant of the necessity of dispelling forever the specter on the horizon.

The modern biologist, engaged in basic research on fundamental problems and elated over his successes, may have overlooked the possibility that the society in which he flourishes might not always be willing to give him its wholehearted support. The present trends in biological research are primarily centered on the attainment of complete mastery over the environment and the control of man's evolution, and to this end life itself is being reduced conceptually to chemical and mathematical abstractions. Is it not conceivable that this activity may result in a world so bleak and so devoid of human values that mankind, in its frustration, would take no further interest in scientific progress? A future world without scientific activity may be unthinkable at the present time, but this activity, having existed for only four centuries, is a very recent and possibly temporary field of human endeavor; it cannot be regarded as an absolute necessity either for man's happiness or survival. If the present trends in scientific research are carried to their logical conclusion, society may one day be forced by science itself to seek its basic interests in other fields of human endeavor. And there is no one today who knows whether mankind would lose or gain by such a change.

The Crossroad Image

On the basis of the foregoing remarks, a mental image may be formed of the modern biologist at the crossroads. The path leading straight ahead, the path which most biologists are taking without having noticed the intersection, leads to an accumulation of factual knowledge in order to master the environment, to alter life at will, and to direct our own evolution. It also leads to the alleviation of physical suffering and privation through progress in medicine and agriculture, just as surely as it leads to an increased materialism primarily concerned with technology and scientific abstraction. From the point of view of humanistic ideals, this road appears to have only one redeeming feature—the betterment of man's physical state. Many biologists will maintain that this is, assuredly, sufficient justification for continuing straight ahead by the most rapid means at our disposal. But if the improved well-being of mankind is to be attained by a continuation and intensification of present biological trends, the accumulation of unforeseen and undesired changes in our world might well defeat the original plan.

Other biologists will hold that moral values will, of necessity, gradually come to the fore to keep pace with scientific progress, but in view of the total eclipse of morality in our recent practical applications of nuclear physics, this seems to be only wishful thinking. Finally, many biologists will be of the opinion that the crossroad image is merely a fanciful illusion; that only one road exists simply because it is an unalterable part of man's nature to be curious about the objective world; that "ye shall know the truth, and the truth shall make you free"; and that, regardless of the consequences, the pursuit of truth must, and will, continue at an ever increasing pace so long as man exists. It is precisely this argument, so admirable and yet so irresponsible, that has prompted the present discussion.

Since it cannot be disputed that the pursuit of scientific truths is a praiseworthy endeavor, why, then, should we hesitate to give it our wholehearted support? It is because the modern biologist, in a kind of blind compulsion, overemphasizes the importance of his activity and fails to perceive that scientific knowledge has less ultimate value for the human race than knowledge of himself. And without self-knowledge, all his objective knowledge of living material and all the practical applications accruing therefrom will count for little—rather, the intensified pursuance of his work and the ensuing devaluation of human ideals for which he will be responsible might well be catastrophic for mankind. Contrary to present trends of thought, biologists are actually under no compulsion to follow the path of "band-wagon" research. There is another road open to them—one that is less obvious and more arduous, but which, I feel, would surely lead to more fertile fields.

The Alternative Road

This alternative road also leads to the attainment of biological truths, but with this difference: that humanistic ideals, rather than scientific knowledge, would be the basis and the *raison d'être* of scientific activity. In other words, biology would not be pursued for its own sake alone but as a means to a higher end: the recognition and realization of the biologist's human potentialities. To place in this way man at the center of things is to accept neither Toynbee's censorious definition of humanism as "man worship"[3] nor the geneticists' concept of humanism as the artificial production of a physically superior being. The primary concern here is rather with the biologist's mental attitude toward his activity in the hope that by recognizing in its proper perspective the place of biology in our modern world, he will adjust the pursuit of his activity accordingly. Through biological research, natural curiosity can be satisfied and material benefit to mankind can accrue; but carried along by the triumphant tide of optimism and success, we have come to view these goals in a false perspective: they have assumed monstrous proportions, far out of keeping with their actual value to mankind.

It is my sincere conviction that the accumulation of scientific knowledge, and its practical application, are and ever will be subordinate to the task of producing whole men—human beings who keenly feel the necessity of going slowly through life, sampling as best they can its rich abundance, and deliberately giving themselves time for reflection on ultimate human values. The single-minded devotion of the modern biologist to his primary concern of making new biological advances in rapid succession and duly reporting them in scientific journals can never be conducive to the full realization of his human potentialities and is, furthermore, an immature conception of what is fitting in the realm of human conduct. Assuming, therefore, that the infusion of a humanistic spirit into the biologist's mental approach to his field would be desirable, what prospects exist for its accomplishment? I suggest that one possible means of doing so would be to introduce into biological thinking a credo of self-restraint—a suggestion which is made in the full realization that any form of biological restraint, be it voluntary or imposed, would be antithetic to the tenets of modern science.

Biological Sophrosyne

The word "restraint" has been chosen for want of a better word in the English language, but actually the Greek word σωφροσύνη (sophrosyne) is more appropriate. Sophrosyne cannot be translated by a single word: the variety of meanings which have been attributed to it include a sane mind, practical wisdom, clear vision, right judgment, self-restraint, moderation, and temperance, as well as humility, humanity, mercy, and modesty. The particular signification desired in the present context can best be elucidated by quoting two Greek scholars. Werner Jaeger in his great work, *Paideia*, interprets the Delphic inscription "Know Thyself" as the doctrine of sophrosyne with these pertinent words:

> It is a mistake to believe that Greek sophrosyne was produced by the naturally harmonious character of the Greek people. . . . The moderation that Apollo preached was not the humdrum doctrine of peace and contentment. It was a strong repression of the new individualistic impulse to wantonness; for in the Apolline code the worst of outrages against heaven was "not to think human thoughts"—to aspire too high, beyond the limits fixed for man.[4]

And are the modern scientist's dreams of disclosing the secrets of life and death, of reducing life to mathematical, physical, and chemical abstractions, of the technological, materialistic world in the making, of supermen and space travel—are these "human thoughts"? I think not, despite the fact that such thoughts are now so deeply rooted in our modern civilization that they have become among its primary considerations. If this were not so, the pursuit of science would be a far less fashionable occupation than it is today.

But even more relevant to the present discussion is a wise and pregnant observation by Gilbert Murray:

> There is a way of thinking which destroys and a way which saves. The man or woman who is sôphrôn walks among the beauties and perils of the world, feeling the love, joy, anger, and the rest; and through it all he has that in his mind which saves. Whom does it save? Not him only, but, as we should say, the whole situation. It saves the imminent evil from coming to be.[5]

The point I would like to make is this: A leading modern biologist, engaged with his team of coworkers in the study of so-called fundamental problems sponsored by governmental or private grants, spending a good portion of his time traveling about to international or *intime* scientific meetings, fully realizing that the pursuit of science today is a business in which personal contacts and politics are necessities, annually publishing a number of scientific papers of a high standard, considering new advances in the fields of biochemistry, biophysics, and biochemical genetics as "exciting," silently passing over contributions dealing with comparative morphology, life cycles, phylogeny, or taxonomy as being devoid of real interest and rather quaint, welcoming graduate students in his department as much for the sake of his own prestige as for their eventual contributions, encouraging his subordinates to follow him in the pursuit of fashionable research problems, being slightly proud of his wholehearted devotion to his work and of his consequent inability to find time for much else than science, and fervently believing in the ever increasing support of "fundamental biological research" in the fixed idea that, come what may, nothing can be more important than an organized and high-pressured attack upon the secrets of life—such a man, I say, is not sophron. And, what is more, he probably couldn't care less. But some of us care, for it is such men who are today largely responsible for determining and directing the future of biology, and therefore of much else.

If they would retort that the problems of biology will be all the more rapidly solved through ever increasing scientific organization, projects, financial support, and teamwork, one must agree. But it can be added that if these trends are followed, it will be at the cost of something of greater value than the scientific problems to be solved—namely, at the cost of realizing our human potentialities, since for this there would be no time. In the general scheme of things in heaven and on earth, does it really matter whether the complete molecular configuration of DNA be known tomorrow or a hundred years hence? The sublimity of the noblest human efforts in the ages preceding the emergence of scientific knowledge seems to make the supreme importance that the modern biologist attaches to the rapid solution of "fundamental" problems appear exaggerated, if not slightly ludicrous. On the other hand, biological sophrosyne, with its emphasis on moderation and restraint, might well give biologists time to recognize what is more important, by any standard, than scientific progress: the first duty of human beings, the nurturing of the divine spark we all have within us. And the fulfillment of this duty during one's lifetime, transcending sophrosyne, becomes, I think, the essence of humanism.

I believe, then, that the pursuit and the attainment of biological truths are a subsidiary field of human endeavor, however fascinating and remunerative it has proved to be. But now, biology, by virtue of its unparalleled success, can no longer be considered merely interesting and beneficial. It has emerged as a source of potential dangers, which, to reiterate, are (1) the reduction of the concept of life to mathematical, physical, and chemical abstractions, (2) the ultimate control of our own physical destiny by artificial regulation of the distribution of human genes, and (3) an overemphasis of the ultimate value of biology with its consequent degradation of humanistic ideals.

Modern biology appears to be getting out of hand, to be running away with us, and we have suggested that biologists could regain control by following an alternative path, where humanistic ideals would have precedence over scientific progress. The rate of scientific advance would thus be automatically retarded, a consequence sure to be considered as heresy by biologists afflicted with band-wagon psychosis and probably by those who are in sympathy with the views of Teilhard de Chardin,[6] but possibly as a harmless, or even welcome, innovation by others. In the belief that the "way of thinking which saves" should be a part of the biologist's mental attitude toward his work, I have further proposed that biological thinking be tempered with self-restraint. In practical terms, what, specifically, would this mean?

First and foremost, it would mean a devaluation of biology's position in modern society through a de-emphasis, if not renunciation, of the corrupting aspects of present-day biological research. Here would be included "fundamental" problems, international congresses, extravagant financial support, power and influence, fame and prestige.

Corrupting Aspects of Biology

The modern biologist's mania for fundamental research problems, which today are primarily concerned with the chemical or physical basis of life, has already been noted. Although there can be no quarrel with a natural interest in problems which are basic by common consent, the present preoccupation with biochemical and biophysical problems to the neglect of almost every other form of biological research is to be deplored. Barry Commoner has recently come to the defense of classical biology by calling attention to the views of men worth listening to—Elsasser, Niels Bohr, and Hinshelwood—and has concluded that since life must be inherently unique, it is an error to suppose that it "is essentially nothing more than an expression of the chemistry of nucleic acid," and that "we cannot study the property of life without retaining it in our experiments."[7] In this age of DNA, how refreshing is his plea that classical biology, being in itself fundamental, is worthy of being saved from engulfment by physics and chemistry. And how apt is his distinction between classical biology and the fashionable biological research problems of today "which surround themselves with glamour." It can only be added that the exercise of reflection and restraint in choosing a field of biological interest is surely preferable to jumping blindly onto the band wagon—lucrative positions, prestige, and fame notwithstanding. A renewed interest in those generally neglected fields of biology known as natural history would undoubtedly go far in restoring to the biologist a feeling of respect for life as well as a sense of humility before its multitudinous aspects.

To speak of the corrupting influence of international scientific congresses will undoubtedly be considered by many as gross exaggeration—yet consider: Their primary purpose is the rapid dissemination of information and the discussion of new advances, but since it is unthinkable that the results discussed will not soon afterward appear in print, and since the public discussions are always limited by the available time, the actual scientific benefits to the participant are often meager. Of course, personal contacts are made, and jobs are secured; by active verbal participation one has the opportunity of appearing brilliant in the eyes of one's colleagues. One has the chance of being seen with the "right" people, and of seeing the world at someone else's expense. But such considerations scarcely justify the elaborate and costly preparation for these congresses. In the belief that international congresses, or for that matter all large scientific congresses, are in reality not much more than oversized shows typical of the age in which we live, I again revert to the advisability of restraint with respect to such enterprises. Actually, when scientific problems and results are in question, much more can usually be accomplished by personal visits to colleagues, especially with the ease and rapidity of modern travel.

As for the desire for fame and prestige, influence and power, and the questionable methods often employed in attaining them, it would be dishonest not to admit their frequent presence in biology, just as in any other field of human endeavor. Yet scientists have the reputation of being disinterested searchers after the truth and, therefore, in them such attributes somehow appear more unseemly and out of place than in other men. And it is precisely for this reason that the passage from Plato quoted at the head of this chapter seems peculiarly apposite.

Scientific Publication

Finally, a word about the publication of scientific results. By common consent the modern scientist is quite unable to cope with the vast number of publications annually appearing in his own specialized sphere of interest, to say nothing of those in related fields and those on more general subjects. Of course, it cannot be otherwise in this flourishing age of science in which so many people have so many things to say. As mentioned above, biologists consider themselves disinterested searchers after the truth and are so regarded by the society in which they live. It must therefore follow that they publish their results for the sole purpose of contributing to mankind's common store of scientific knowledge. But is this essentially true? If it were, scientists should be quite willing to publish anonymously—something which the majority, naturally desirous of their due share of fame, most certainly would not do.

In any modern scientific institution the advancement of a scientist depends, naturally enough, upon his scientific contributions; but mere number of publications may be of equal or greater importance than quality, so that the number of times his name appears in print is often an index of his prestige, his position, and his salary. Thus, the published word has a direct relation to the material well-being of the modern biologist, a system which naturally encourages, along with first-class contributions, the publication of trivialities and works of doubtful value. If anonymous scientific writing were the established custom, it is probable that the number of papers published annually would be far less than it is today. I am not, however, claiming either the feasibility or the advisability of anonymity in authorship but merely focusing attention upon the mental approach of many biologists toward their activity.

It is interesting to compare the practice of authors in the ancient world. Hebrew literature, for example, was chiefly anonymous until well into the Christian era, and the impersonality of its productive energy was based upon the belief that the importance of the subject matter (here primarily the Old Testament) so transcended that of the author that any association with his name would defile rather than embellish. And with respect to the unknown authors who worked over the *Iliad*, Gilbert Murray has written: "He gave his name, as he gave all else that was in him, to help, unnoticed, in the building up of the greatest poem that ever sounded on the lips of men."[8] Not that the building up of the storehouse of scientific knowledge through the accumulation of objective truths can be directly compared with the creation of a literary masterpiece, but it is at least worth reflecting upon the antithetic attitudes arising in these two fields of human endeavor, separated in time by two millennia. Each writer believed that his subject was of utmost significance for the society in which he lived, and each believed himself to be a disinterested author, yet it was the ancient, not the modern, who acted more in accordance with his beliefs.

The Need for a Renewal in Biological Thinking

Hitherto, in discussing the desired changes in biological thinking, I have primarily dwelt on negative criticism—and that probably in a manner copious enough to arouse antagonism or displeasure in the reader, who may feel that it amounts to little more than moralizing and attempting to turn back the clock. I do not deny having made moral reflections, but I am not trying to turn back the clock. The views expressed have rather been an attempt to demonstrate the urgency of a renewal in biological thinking—a renewal involving neither obscurantism nor fear of new objective truths, but rather the evaluation of scientific progress in a saner perspective, through the realization that the most precious things in life lie outside its domain. Science should advance, not with unseemly haste and indiscriminate activity, and not with the end justifying the means, but in a manner which, above all, is fitting and subordinate to the ideals of humanism.

If the biologist's reflections eventually bring him to the conclusion that elevating the importance of humanistic ideals is synonymous with minimizing the importance of biology, and if he acts accordingly, what are the chief advantages apart from the repression of corruptive influences that stand to be gained? *To modern society:* by the gradual extinction of the immanent perils in modern biology, the hope of a saner and more humanized world. *To the modern biologist:* by the gradual realization of his human potentialities, the hope of evolving into a whole man.

These hopes are in no way original. Down through the centuries they have been thundered at mankind in various ways by those who felt they had a message of importance to convey to an erring world. In modern times, as in the past, these hopes have been expressed by men imbued with idealism—Albert Schweitzer,[9] for example, with his repeated emphasis on respect for life; or Loren Eiseley,[10] whose essay, "The Bird and the Machine," should be required reading for all biologists; or Benjamin Farrington,[11] with his recent plea for a renewed study of the humanities; or Lewis Mumford,[12] whose inspired views on the meaning and the renewal of life and on the whole man are a landmark in twentieth-century thought. In the face of the force and eloquence of these and similar messages, the moral indignation which prompted the present attempt is necessarily tempered with humility. But in the belief that biology—this one facet of human activity—would do well to subordinate its present goals to the realization of the latent magnificence that already exists within us, also this attempt had to be made. It is for the biologist to decide whether it has been worthwhile.

II

Positive Eugenics and Evolution

Man is still very much an unfinished type, who clearly has actualized only a small fraction of his human potentialities. . . . Man, in fact, is in urgent need of further improvement.
—Sir Julian Huxley, Galton Lecture, 1962.

Self-Improvement and Human Progress

The words quoted above echo a sentiment which has been repeatedly expressed in a variety of ways for more than two millennia and, for all we know, may have been thought or uttered during untold ages before human desires were recorded. For the need of self-improvement is life's challenge to each succeeding generation, and since an awareness of this problem and a desire to solve it seem to be an essential part of our evolutionary development, we will in all probability ever continue to grope after the answer.

For six thousand years the evolutionary progress of civilized man was based upon the slow, cumulative transmission of the cultural and ideological aspects of human experience; only in the recent past has it become increasingly rapid through the acquisition and transmission of scientific knowledge. Yet any serious consideration of human progress in the Scientific Age reveals that something is amiss. Being aware that our accelerating development during the last four hundred years has been primarily intellectual, and being unable to find the necessary balance and harmony between the realm of the intellect and that of the spirit, we are for the first time faced with the prospect of self-annihilation or, perhaps worse still, of regression to a dehumanized state. Passive acceptance of the evolutionary concept of automatic and perpetual human "progress" no longer suffices in the second half of the twentieth century. Reflections on the future of Homo sapiens are required more than ever before.

Many proposals for improvement of the species were offered to mankind in good faith by the most enlightened minds of the Pre-Scientific World and transmitted as part of our heritage. One such proposal, put forward nearly twenty-five hundred years ago in a shockingly dogmatic way by Plato, was revived in a milder form in the nineteenth century when Sir Francis Galton suggested that our physical and mental condition could be best improved by what he termed eugenics, according to which the unfit were discouraged and the fit encouraged to reproduce. The enthusiastic interest which greeted Galton's proposal has continued down to the present. At the same time, advances in genetics, as in nearly all other branches of science, have been so explosive that the geneticist, in cooperation with the biologist, the biochemist, and the medical scientist, is now in a position to elaborate human breeding programs on a scale probably undreamed of by Plato or Galton.

Swept along by the triumphant march of science and fervently believing in the necessity of a scientific attack upon all of life's unexplained aspects, the advocates of positive eugenics are vociferous, insistent, and very well-meaning. They sincerely believe that positive eugenics not only affords the greatest hope for man's improvement but that it would also tend to dissipate the perils which confront him. In their enthusiasm for science, they are led to the conclusion that the scientific regulation of human reproduction by artificial means is the most rapid way we can realize our potentialities and that the day must soon come when world opinion will adopt this solution as a moral imperative. With equal sincerity, I believe that to adopt this way out of our difficulties would not only be immoral but would tend to efface our human potentialities. The purpose of this chapter, which deals primarily with the views expressed in Sir Julian Huxley's Galton Lecture,[1] is, therefore, to state my reasons for believing that positive eugenics, as advocated by twentieth-century scientists, would do mankind more harm than good.

To avoid ambiguity, it is well to state at the outset that the eugenists' proposals which come under the heading "negative eugenics" and which include reducing man-made radiation and discouraging genetically defective individuals from reproducing as well as the attempt to reduce human overmultiplication—all of these have my sympathy. But let us now turn to positive eugenics and consider it in the broadest possible perspective—that of evolution.

The Scientist's View of Human Evolution

Near the conclusion of the Galton Lecture these words occur: "All the objections of principle to a policy of positive eugenics fall to the ground when the subject is looked at in the embracing perspective of evolution. . . ." I find it impossible to agree with this statement. It is, of course, quite true, as Huxley points out, that the biological phase of human evolution has been supplemented by the psychosocial phase, and that the acquisition and transmission of knowledge and culture are now occurring so rapidly that our thinking is becoming revolutionized. The astounding advance of science and its practical application seem to have convinced us that not only is human progress chiefly dependent upon the continued accumulation of objective knowledge, but that the fulfillment of our destiny is inevitably linked to this activity. Man, evolving more swiftly than ever before, realizes his perils yet moves forward in confidence, for he believes it impossible to stem the tide and unthinkable to wish to do so.

Teilhard de Chardin,[2] in his concept of the inevitable acceleration of mental activity ("noogenesis") as a necessary prelude to the evolution of true men ("hominization"), supported this point of view and expressed it probably more profoundly than anyone else; and although the world at large is unaware of his evolutionary doctrine, it supports his belief in the compelling necessity of intellectual achievement. For the world outlook today follows the lead of science and accordingly exhibits an insatiate desire for intellectual novelty and an unreflecting acquiescence in all means necessary for its rapid attainment. It equates human evolutionary progress with a kind of predestined intellectual development, omnipotent and all-embracing, which is carrying us along in a straight line toward a scientifically directed world, whether all of us approve or not. The manifest fact that contemporary world thought is dominated by the scientific outlook can, I think, be justly regarded as the most serious obstacle of our age to true human progress.

Huxley, on the other hand, maintains that scientific progress is primarily responsible for man's having already evolved sufficiently to have attained a "new and unified vision of reality, both fuller and truer than any of the insights of the past," and that therefore he should not only be willing to entrust science with the artificial control of his reproduction but that it is, indeed, part of his destiny to do so. Yet if insight means discernment, mental vision, or intuition, I would consider his above statement far too sweeping. Our present insight into reality, although obviously more complete than any in the past, is disproportionately one-sided: it arises primarily from the factual knowledge derived from scientific activity and, therefore, is not and cannot be directly concerned with spiritual values. If it were, our Scientific

Age would already have witnessed a renewal of our ethical code, which Heitler has demanded with so much justification,[3] rather than its increasing relaxation. However much our acquired knowledge of the physical world may have induced speculation about the spiritual world, it most certainly has not given men any insight which has made them more virtuous.

An Alternative View of Human Evolution

It seems to me, therefore, that human evolution can be viewed in quite another perspective, and one which directly opposes the policy of positive eugenics. Instead of taking for granted that it is man's destiny to direct his future on the basis of increasing scientific knowledge, I would rather say that it is man's destiny to recognize that when his progress once becomes steadily intellectual rather than moral, it is time that he direct his future away from the dominance of science. Psychosocial evolution need not be in a straight line, and recognition and rectification of error should be part of *Homo sapiens'* maturity.

In the last hundred years we have come so far so fast that we must now pause to consider whether our present path does actually lead toward the realization of our potentialities. At least we should be aware that we now have a choice: either going straight ahead, continuing to regard the realm of the intellect as supreme and fondly hoping that our moral code will somehow keep pace with our advances, or diverging to regard the realm of the spirit as supreme and thereby devaluating the importance of science through exercise of restraint in its pursuit. Making such a choice would necessarily involve, among other things, an answer to the following question: Although we are now sufficiently intelligent to attempt to direct our future by scientifically controlled breeding, are we sufficiently human to do so? I would say emphatically that we are not. And to this I would add that when we are, we will have no need for positive eugenics. Moreover, I believe that we will actually become less human if we refuse to resist the compulsive forces and trends which continually emanate from the cult of Scientific Progress and which are intuitively felt—by some of us, at least—to be unnatural and immoral. It must be remembered that the mental outlook which enthusiastically welcomes every scientific novelty and unhesitatingly demands its practical application was responsible for the development of the atomic bomb. However much one may argue that the atomic bomb, or its successors, can safeguard the peace, no one can seriously maintain that the world is a better place with it. For it has been used.

The mental outlook of the positive eugenists invites comparison: What we can do, we must do! Yet once a sperm and egg bank is put to use, the damage is done, and the world will forever have with it what it would be better off without—descendants of human beings who are artificially produced according to the whims and fancies and expert advice of one particular generation whose moral code was overshadowed by its enthusiasm for science. Positive eugenists nevertheless insist that the appearance upon the earth of such human beings and their progeny would represent a rapid and inevitable advance in the evolution of man, for some of these individuals, if not eventually all, would necessarily be more "human" than we. Let us consider this point.

The Human Potential and Superior Humanness

Everyone would agree that evolution, in the case of man, is synonymous with becoming more human. But what, actually, does this mean? What is the meaning of the oft-repeated phrase, "the realization (or actualization) of our human potentialities"? This question is not at all easy to answer. In the first place, we have no direct genetic basis for human potentialities and their realization, for we cannot attribute them to specific genes and their action. Secondly, much of what is included in any concept of the ideal human potential stems from difficultly expressible intuitions, attitudes, and emotions. Yet certainly a part of the answer should include that inherently satisfying idea of the "whole man," which Mumford has so beautifully expressed.[4] I think it would also be well to emphasize that the increasing humanness of the future, both on the individual and the evolutionary level, will have to be concerned more with virtue than with intelligence.

As a tentative definition one might suggest that to become more human means the slow and laborious approach to the divine through an increasing awareness of one's own immortal spark and of the spiritual heights already attained by mankind. This is in no way meant to disparage the physical and intellectual aspects of human evolution, for a race of healthy and intelligent men is a necessary part of it—but by no means all. What matters most is in the realm of the spirit. The most outstanding and enlightened human figures have not been merely intelligent: they have also been aware that the essential thing in life both for themselves and for future generations is to make the spark to glow through preoccupation with love, virtue, and the right choice.

We have no reason to suppose that such individuals will not continue to appear infrequently in future generations. Positive eugenists, however, are impatient and discontent with present psychosocial progress and the slowness and haphazardness with which natural selection "blindly and automatically" operates, and therefore wish to hasten and direct both evolutionary processes through unnatural selection by means of artificial redistribution of unknown human genes. Since their knowledge of human genetics is insufficient to allow them to breed extensively for single, specific characters, they hope that by employing sex cells selected from outstanding individuals, they can raise the general genetic level and thereby ensure more rapid production of more outstanding individuals.

The crucial point here seems to be what criteria are to be used in evaluating the superior humanness of an outstanding individual. Since inheritance of human intelligence and physical traits has long been observed, positive eugenics might conceivably be able to raise the intelligence quotient of man and to alter his physical state; yet I cannot believe that these are the essential criteria of becoming more human. A mere increase in the proportion of healthy super-intellectuals will not suffice for future human progress, for in the absence or neglect of love and virtue, such "outstanding" individuals will never be more human than we. After stating that their aim is to produce more and "better" scientists, artists, writers, statesmen, technologists, and engineers, Julian Huxley does, however, say that "for more and better saints and moral leaders, [we need the raising of the genetic level] of disciplined valuation, of devotion and duty, and of the capacity to love. . . ."[5] And I would say that positive eugenists, despite their earnest intentions, know nothing—absolutely nothing—about the genetic basis of love and virtue and that it is misleading to the world at large even to include such human traits in a prospectus of their policy.

Human Arete

Actually, such traits—the most significant of all for human evolution—may, for all we know, have no direct genetic basis at all. History records numerous instances of human beings who are remembered for their virtue and nobility of character but whose offspring (and/or parents) were either morally neutral or actually immoral and degenerate. As pointed out long ago by Socrates, that rare combination of extreme virtue, intelligence, and emotion, which is called human *arete** and which has ever distinguished the truly outstanding individual, does not appear to be

---

* The Greek word ἀρετή, when applied to a human being, denotes his supreme excellence and cannot be adequately translated by a single word.

inherited. Twentieth-century geneticists would undoubtedly attribute *arete* to some rare combination of genes, but in the complete absence of proof of such a contention, one can with equal justification regard it, at least in part, as non-genic. Therefore, while I agree wholeheartedly with Huxley in attaching so much importance to "outstanding, gifted individuals," and with his view that our future progress is partly dependent upon the psychosocial transmission of their creative efforts, I do not agree with him that individuals are outstanding primarily because of their genic complement provided by natural selection. The most outstanding ones appear to have in addition some sort of heightened awareness of their immortal spark and their spiritual heritage, and this attribute seems to be non-inherited and psychosocially activated.

It is even conceivable that one of the unrecognized mechanisms of human evolution might be the appearance in its psychosocial phase of individuals who possess such an attribute over and above genetically determined intelligence. Without it, man's highest potentialities cannot be realized and the highest *arete* cannot exist. Little wonder that both Pindar and Socrates consider that human *arete* might be a gift of the gods! For it does appear to be man's closest approach to the divine, and therefore any desire to breed for it by elevating the genetic level to produce saints and moral leaders seems misdirected, if not arrogant. Whatever its origin, it has appeared, unbidden and unexpected, at rare moments during the psychosocial phase of evolution as one of mankind's supreme blessings—and it will undoubtedly continue to do so. It seems to me to indicate a blatant disrespect for life itself when twentieth-century scientists confidently envisage the day when a combination of luck and applied genetics will enable them to produce not only super-intellectuals but a Plato or a Christ as well.

The Dehumanizing Consequences of the Eugenists' Proposals

We must, however, face the possibility that if the policy of positive eugenists were adopted, their systematized efforts would eventually result in such a wealth of data concerning the inheritance of human characters that some kind of correlation between genes and spiritual traits might conceivably be discovered. This, of course, is one of their aims; and whether it is fulfilled or not, the result would be the intrusion of modern science into the realm of spiritual values, which are subjective and therefore properly outside its domain. The prospect of the passions, ideals, emotions, and behavior of a human life being classified, card-indexed, or electronically coded typifies as well as anything else the dehumanizing trend of thought of the Scientific Age.

It must also be remembered that such data, enthusiastically collected and assiduously studied, would be employed to investigate not only the genetics of virtue but of evil also. It could not be otherwise in a world which fervently believes in the desirability of a scientific attack upon all aspects of life. And were this knowledge available and combined with genetic data concerning intelligence and physical traits, what guarantee can positive eugenists give us that further human breeding would forever be planned and directed by morally superior individuals or groups? In a world obsessed by the belief that science is the supreme panacea, serious reflection on the misuse that could be made of such knowledge is by no means obscurantism. It is not only difficult to accept the view that positive eugenics would necessarily result in a higher frequency of individuals who are more human, but easy to imagine that world-wide preoccupation with such a policy would actually hinder us from realizing the human potentialities we already possess.

In fact, I do not think there are any convincing arguments by which positive eugenists can minimize the dangers inherent in their policy. All of the serious problems regarding paternity and maternity (the successful engrafting of deep-frozen ova into women is anticipated) and the overthrow of traditional social conventions are too obvious even to discuss. So, too, is the possibility that geneticists will one day succeed in inducing directed gene mutation at will. But probably the most fundamental objection, operative at the very inception of a breeding program, would be the selection of sex cells. Julian Huxley writes:

> There will be no single types to be selected for, but a range of preferred types; and this will not be chosen by a single individual or committee. The choice will be a collective choice representing the varied preferences and ideals of all the couples practicing euselection . . . [and] as general acceptance of the method grows it will be reinforced by public opinion and official leadership. . . . The way is open for the most significant step in the progress of mankind—the deliberate improvement of the species by scientific and democratic methods.[6]

Thus Plato's dictatorial suggestion that the city-state control the reproduction of its inhabitants appears in modern guise: the substitution of scientific for governmental control. Public opinion is already dominated by the scientific outlook, and as all couples naturally desire healthy, intelligent offspring, they could appeal only to science for guidance in making their final choice. However democratic the selection might appear to be, both with regard to the sex cells to be stored and those to be used, it would, in the final analysis, represent a scientific evaluation of "desirable" human traits and their heritability.

Today we are so far from realizing our human potentialities that we are quite incapable of coping with the factual knowledge science has already placed at our disposal. The existence of nuclear weapons confirms this fact. It is confirmed in the current eugenic belief that it is fitting human conduct to employ for breeding purposes the living sex cells of individuals long since dead. And it is again confirmed by the statement that "shelters for sperm banks will give better genetic results than shelters for people, as well as being very much cheaper."[7] Let us first elevate and intensify our humanness before deciding whether our reproduction should be based upon methods determined by science or by human love.

Other Means of Promoting Human Evolution

I am convinced that we can increase our humanness—without recourse to positive eugenics, and even if our future evolution should fail to produce more truly outstanding individuals. For the potentialities already existing within each one of us represent latent magnificence more than sufficient for one's lifetime. Whatever a man's genetic make-up, he is uniquely human and therefore in possession of an immortal spark and a spiritual heritage. While outstanding individuals know that these are their most precious possessions, most men lead lives in unawareness of them. Yet awareness of these possessions could enable a man to become more human—if he so desires. The crucial fact of our age, it seems to me, is that man at last can be made to so desire, not by science providing him with a novel genic complement, but by education kindling his spark through renewed emphasis on his spiritual heritage and thereby providing him with the knowledge that human *arete* is a supreme good which he cannot afford to live without.

A desire to utilize one's own potencies in order to attain *arete* is at the same time a desire to become more human. The most sublime forms of *arete* have been exhibited by those individuals who were able to realize their highest potentialities through an intense and lifelong devotion to spiritual values. This ability may be divinely inspired, but whatever its origin, Jaeger expressed a profound truth in the simple statement that once a human potentiality is realized, it exists[8]—for the existing *arete* of the past is our touchstone of humanness. All men cannot be outstanding. Yet all men, through knowledge of superior humanness, could know what it means to be a human being and that, as such, they too have a contribution to make. It is magnificent to become as human as one is able. And it requires no help from science. In addition, the very act of realizing one's potentialities might constitute an advance over what has gone before.

For it is not the genetic aspect of evolution with which we should now be concerned, even if for the first time we are able to alter and redirect it. That which the positive eugenists hope most to do—to raise the general genetic level and thereby man's intelligence quotient—would only increase the alarming disproportion between intelligence and virtue which already exists. For spiritual traits, whether accidentally or deliberately a part of the eugenists' breeding program, are not the concern of modern science. We will never improve the species by attempting a scientific exploration of the spiritual world. But we could improve the species by altering and redirecting the psychosocial aspect of evolution—and it is this task which should demand our unceasing attention from now on. Twenty years ago Huxley, without referring to positive eugenics, wrote: "Man can inject his ethics into the heart of evolution"[9]; and this I believe to be true.

We are already sufficiently mature to begin to evaluate and select the most precious parts of our culture that need to be emphasized in the psychosocial transmission of the future. Recognition and appreciation of the superior humanness of the past would go further toward realizing our existing potentialities than any amount of well-meaning genic tampering. Yet as long as we continue to allow the scientific outlook to dominate our thinking, we will ever believe that the ends justify the means and that intellectual novelty is the ultimate value—and we will never be the more human for that. To diminish the exaggerated prestige of science, to pursue it with restraint, to be aware of the social and moral responsibilities its application entails, and above all, to know that the chief motive for scientific research, or any other human activity, is to realize the individual's existing potentialities—such a renewal in contemporary thought seems to be required today.

It is hoped that the above views will not be misinterpreted as a lack of sympathy with the earnest and sincere motives of the positive eugenists. I am sure that our basic aims are identical—to augment the humanness of man—and that it is primarily the means advocated which provoke disagreement. At this stage of human history neither side can validate its views, and therefore faith, intuition, and emotion, whether acknowledged or not, play a necessary role in all the speculative arguments advanced. Yet, for some, the choice will ever lie between a future world directed by those who, neglecting their own heritage and potentialities, find their most intense satisfaction in contributing to continued scientific progress and its application; and a future world directed by those who have been educated to find most joy in knowing of man's previous attainments in his approach to the divine and in realizing that what they have within themselves will suffice for their own brief sojourn on this earth. The latter would, I think, nod approvingly to the opening strains of that rarely beautiful English madrigal of the seventeenth century:

> Thus angels sung,
> And thus sing we. . . .

III

The Utilization of Animals in Medical Research

And I will keep pure and holy both my life and my art.
—*Hippocrates.*

Historical Introduction

During the six thousand years of man's civilized state his relationship to the higher animals that make up a part of his living environment has become increasingly diversified. The necessity of satisfying his primary demands for sustenance has compelled him to hunt down the wild animals within his reach, to domesticate many of them, and to breed new types for his special uses, besides employing them in hunting and war, for labor and transport, and as guards and companions. Animals have also long been used in sport, and in ancient Rome horse exhibitions and chariot races drew enthusiastic crowds to the circus, from which the modern animal circus, originating in the eighteenth century, derives its name. Likewise, the gladiatorial spectacles of the ancient world necessitated the capture and transport of wild animals from remote and often difficultly accessible areas. The practice of keeping both endemic and exotic animals in captivity for man's amusement and edification apparently arose *de novo* on more than one occasion, for a Chinese emperor of the twelfth century B.C. and an English king of the twelfth century A.D. each had his own zoological garden, and Prescott reports that in the sixteenth century Montezuma kept a large zoo in his capital in Mexico.[1]

The intellectual curiosity which animals have aroused in man has also resulted in their having been described and illustrated for more than two thousand years, as well as grouped and classified according to their external appearance. Internally, they are known to have been studied as far back as the time of Aristotle, and Singer states that in the third century B.C. animal dissections were practiced also by Greek anatomists in Alexandria.[2] Four hundred years later the anatomy and physiology of the Barbary ape were extensively studied by Galen, the physician of Marcus Aurelius. In the thousand years that followed there is little record of this relationship of man to animals, but in the fourteenth century the anatomist Mondino dissected pigs and dogs at Bologna, and one important contribution of the sixteenth century was Leonardo da Vinci's work as a comparative anatomist. In the sixteenth and seventeenth centuries comparative anatomy flourished in many European centers concurrently with the rise of modern experimental science. Thereby was initiated a new era in man's relationship to the higher animals: he began to use them in ever increasing numbers as experimental objects of scientific research.

Of considerable historical interest are some figures on the number of animals which were annually employed in physiological and pathological experiments in England and Scotland half a century ago; the figures are no less interesting because of the license or certificate which was required for every animal experiment performed. In 1909, for example, 86,277 animals were employed, of which the great majority were rats, mice, rabbits, and guinea pigs, for at that time dogs, cats, and monkeys were used much less frequently than today; scientific research in the sense of the organization and tempo by which it is now characterized had scarcely got under way. Today the number of animals annually employed in experiments by scientists throughout the world can only be guessed at. The benefits to the health of mankind resulting from all this scientific activity are so well known that they certainly need not be enumerated, and it is not my purpose to do so. My purpose is rather to show that present progress in biological and medical research is often dependent upon means which are retarding the realization of human potentialities and thereby doing mankind more harm than good. To develop this point of view it is first necessary to turn to a recent phenomenon that has been contemporaneous with the period of most rapid progress of medical research and which bears directly upon it: man's growing sensitivity to the infliction of pain and suffering. For this is a phenomenon with which modern science has not yet come to terms.

Objective and Subjective Humaneness

The humaneness of medical science has always expressed itself in an unquestioning and immediate desire to prevent or alleviate human suffering, regardless of whether it is inflicted or arises from natural causes. This humaneness is based upon the accumulated medical knowledge of the past and is augmented only by further accumulation of scientific facts that are employed in the improvement of man's health. In other words, the objectivity of science restricts the further development of the medical scientist's humaneness to the pursuit of knowledge. And, as I will attempt to show, such objective humaneness, while responsible for a tremendous decrease in human suffering, is becoming increasingly dependent upon an inhumaneness that is integral to its further progress. The objectivity of modern science sets scientists, as such, somewhat apart from the rest of mankind and causes them to disregard the growing sensitivity to inflicted cruelty that exists outside of their profession. For the recently acquired humaneness of modern society, which also strives to abolish suffering of any kind, is in no way restricted by scientific objectivity but is inherently subjective and based upon ethical considerations of pain and brutality.

Knowledge of inflicted cruelty today evokes in a vast number of people—and here I am qualified to speak only of Americans and Europeans—a horror and a revulsion that are often accompanied by moral indignation sufficient to organize large-scale movements to suppress the outrage and to prevent its recurrence. It is probably safe to say that most of us, scientists and laymen alike, feel, as human beings, that one of the prime requisites of a better world is the suppression of cruelty. In the absence of past records to the contrary, we can assume that this widespread, common response to pain is of relatively recent date. Formerly, man was more callous to either inflicted or natural physical suffering, regarding it as an inevitable and necessary part of life, to be accepted and endured rather than pitied and suppressed. We have, however, no reason for taking excessive pride in our increasing humaneness, nor for supposing that our growing sensitivity has resulted in a continuous diminution of man-inflicted suffering during the last century or two. We need only recall that nineteenth-century humaneness, which expressed itself, for example, in British legislation for the prevention of cruelty to children, was followed by twentieth-century inhumaneness of unparalleled magnitude, expressing itself in war atrocities and concentration camps. Yet it is nevertheless true that until relatively recent times the desire to diminish man-inflicted suffering was sporadic and incapable of developing into a common human response, while today this desire appears to be a permanent part of the mental outlook of a good proportion of the world population. This new subjective humaneness indicates a change in world consciousness, if not conscience, and there is every reason to believe that this growing compassion, mercy, and tenderness is significant in human evolution.

A satisfying explanation for man having, so to speak, suddenly arrived at this new evolutionary threshold does not come easily. Education is undoubtedly a contributory factor but fails to account for the widespread prevalence of what seems to be an automatic and instinctive hatred of the infliction of suffering. W. R. Inge, the learned Dean of Saint Paul's, while regretfully admitting that Christianity had been in no way responsible for the development of humaneness, suggested that it arose in the eighteenth century as a revolt against the preceding age of "insensibility."[3] This, however, seems too sweeping a generalization, for the insensibility of the seventeenth century was by no means omnipresent: to music, for example, society at that time exhibited a high degree of aesthetic sensitivity. Yet, however we attempt to explain it, the fact remains that more men than ever before are now fully aware of what it means to be humane. For this we should be most grateful. It is a token of our ability to realize our human potentialities.

For the purpose of the present discussion, the significant part of this changed ethical outlook is that man is directing his newly found humaneness not only toward himself but toward other forms of life as well. Admittedly, the first attempts to prevent cruelty to animals were justified on the ground of the demoralizing effect it had upon human spectators (not perpetrators!), but it is worthy to note that in England the first Cruelty to Animals Act was passed in 1822, more than sixty years before the first Cruelty to Children Act. Although many obstructions to the prevention of cruelty to animals have arisen in Catholic countries,*

---

* Dean Inge, in discussing the Catholic church's teaching that "animals have no souls and therefore no rights," reported the disquieting fact that ". . . Pius IX refused to allow the Society for the Prevention of Cruelty to Animals to work in Rome on the ground that it is a theological error to teach that men have any duties toward animals."

many types of active animal welfare societies, often abetted by the excessive enthusiasm or even fanaticism of their members, have been formed in Europe and America. During the same period, legislation has been enacted enforcing humane restrictions on the treatment, transport, hunting, and slaughtering of animals. The result has been that much cruelty to animals, which often stems from ignorance or insensibility, has been prevented—and with relatively little protest.

An entirely different picture emerges from the utilization of animals as experimental objects of medical and biological science. Out of this relationship of man to animals has arisen a conflict between the objective humaneness of modern science and the subjective humaneness of modern society. This problem, the result of an unavoidable clash between two powerful forces of idealism, admits of no facile solution. Let us consider it.

We have, on the one hand, the idealism arising from man's recently acquired interest in humaneness and clearly manifesting itself in public agitation by vociferous animal welfare societies and anti-vivisection groups who are striving by all available means to improve the condition of laboratory animals, both with regard to care and to the types of experiments to which they are subjected. We have, on the other hand, the idealism inherent in medical research, whose unquestioned authority has been gathering momentum for more than three hundred years and whose goal is to acquire by all available means more complete knowledge of the mammalian body in order to improve, through more enlightened care, the health of man and of his domesticated animals. The problem to be solved is how these two forces can best come to terms.

Being neither an animal fanatic nor a member of the medical profession, I am aware that my words may carry no weight with the extremists of either group. It is also possible that anyone whose own hard work has relieved the suffering of either men or of animals may resent the views of one who has done neither. Yet an outsider, in viewing the problem from both perspectives, may possibly contribute to its more general illumination. This, together with an earnest interest in the subject, must serve as the justification of what follows.

The Growing Concern about the Ethics of Animal Experimentation

Organized anti-vivisection groups have existed for more than half a century, and their activity has played a role in influencing both legislation and public opinion relevant to animal experimentation. As a matter of fact, these groups were so powerful in the first decade of the twentieth century that their antagonists, the supporters of animal experimentation, were actually forced in Britain to found the Research Defence Society. While anti-vivisection agitation has continued up to the present day, such acts of self-defense on the part of scientists are no longer necessary. On the contrary, our age has truly become a Scientific Age, in which the attainment of new scientific knowledge by the most rapid means available seems to be the supreme goal. No other human activity today receives more support, both moral and financial, than scientific research; particularly with respect to medicine, it is practically unthinkable that any hindrance should stand in the way of its further progress.

However, in recent years the inevitable consequence of man's growing humaneness has made itself felt by much more than anti-vivisection agitation alone. In the United States, for example, there is violent criticism of the way in which animal experimentation is being carried out in American laboratories, together with pending legislation for more humane treatment of laboratory animals. In Switzerland, the World Federation for the Protection of Animals has reprinted in a recent bulletin an article from an American periodical on the inhumane treatment to which laboratory animals are being subjected. In Japan, there are efforts by

Europeans to promote more humane care of the animals employed by university medical students. In Greece, the 1962–63 Annual Report of the Greek Animal Welfare Fund contains these words: "Only during the last year has the Working Committee found the time and courage to take on the problem of experimental animals inside the hospitals in Athens." In Sweden, the Society for the Prevention of Painful Animal Experimentation has been founded. In Denmark, the National Society for the Protection of Experimental Animals has now been created.

These examples—and there are undoubtedly many more of which I am ignorant—come from outside the scientific profession, but they do not represent the voices of extreme anti-vivisectionists. Admittedly, they may often be unreflecting and officious voices, yet they do appear to express the earnest views of those who realize that laboratory animals often lack adequate housing, care, and feeding, and of those who are awake to the ethical aspect of the problem of "necessary pain" in biological and medical research. It is this second problem, by far the more fundamental of the two, which will be considered here.

The Problem of "Necessary Pain"

Science, having had several centuries to reflect upon the problem of "necessary pain," has, to judge from scientific literature, long since solved it to its own satisfaction. The seemingly unalterable conclusion of many contemporary scientists who employ laboratory animals is that their experiments—in design, methods, and execution—are either beyond reproach or are not even to be judged by ethical standards, for what they do, they must do for the sake of humanity. I doubt very much that such idealism will stand the test of time. It is an idealism which springs directly from objective humaneness and from that deeply ingrained creed of our Scientific Age that it is only the goal that matters. This creed, I am convinced, is destined to be superseded in the fullness of time by a faith that is more in harmony with the realization of the human potential.

One of the basic concepts of the scientific outlook has always been that the ends justify the means, and now in the twentieth century this concept has finally transcended the realm of science to become an integral part of the world outlook. Most people today, be they members of the scientific profession or not, would hold that the desire to restrict or hamper the progress of medical research must stem from a profound lack of knowledge, insight, or humanism, for a pursuit which endeavors to improve the health of man can only be noble, idealistic, and worthy of unlimited support. In other words, since science *can* extend its knowledge in order to alleviate more human pain and prolong more human lives, it *must* do so—and as rapidly as possible and by all the means at its disposal.

I disagree. I believe that our Scientific Age needs not so much to extend its intellectual frontiers as to become aware of man's ultimate goal: to become more human. We can choose between increased factual knowledge gained by wholly unrestricted scientific progress, together with all the benefits to mankind thereby accruing, or increased humanness. But we cannot have both, for the two are incompatible.

To support this conviction, I would like to submit evidence to show that modern biology and medical science, in their blind compulsion to attain new knowledge, are employing means for doing so which are directly harmful to humanity. Let me quote from a recent paper dealing with that fashionable subject of contemporary medical research, pain. Steel electrodes were implanted into the pain perception areas of the brains of anesthetized monkeys; several days after the operation the fully conscious monkeys were placed in "specially designed restraining units" and electrical stimulation was applied through the electrodes. Weitzman and Ross stated that as they increased the current, the monkeys showed "facial grimacing, closure of both eyes, high-pitched vocalization, turning of the head away from the side of the stimulus, and generalized motor activity."[4] I would say that whatever knowledge was acquired from this experiment and however much it might contribute to the alleviation of human suffering, it cannot be justified by any human standard. And if it were maintained that only those actively working in the field are competent to judge whether the inflicted pain was "necessary," I would reply that the experiment was conducted by medical scientists for the benefit of humanity and therefore anyone has the right to judge it—and that in my opinion to design and execute such an experiment represents conduct unworthy of a human being. To describe the screams of tortured animals as "high-pitched vocalization," while impeccable from the standpoint of scientific writing, only adds weight to my argument. Emotionalism? Of course it is. To inject more human feeling into the biologist's mental outlook would give him a far saner perspective than he now possesses with which to evaluate the relative importance of his own activity.

Scientific literature abounds with examples of faith in the contention that the ends justify the means. One more will not be amiss. It involves the experimental production of traumatic shock in dogs,[5] which was undertaken during World War II in the hope of adding to our knowledge of traumatic shock such as had been experienced by military personnel. But the methods of this investigation, in contrast to what befell the soldiers, included the systematic beating of anesthetized dogs with a rawhide mallet. (Its exact weight and dimensions were given for the benefit of colleagues who might be interested in inflicting similar muscular contusions on other dogs. Many were.) Each dog, after having been placed in an unnatural, supine position on the animal table, was anesthetized and then dealt from 700 to 1000 blows on each of its hind legs, which had been depilated. Concerning this treatment the authors wrote: ". . . we sought constantly to standardize the procedure, and although we were able to produce fatal shock consistently in a high percentage of the animals, we never succeeded in eliminating the element of 'feel' or subjective personal judgment from the experiments. As the work progressed it became apparent that the results were most consistent if the injury was applied by the same individual from day to day." For those who are not offended by the infliction of injury under anesthesia, it can be mentioned that immediately after the treatment, the administration of ether was discontinued: in one set of experiments 29 out of 30 dogs experienced shock and 25 of them expired, the survival times of these 25 dogs ranging from 50 minutes to 9 hours and 21 minutes. The authors stated further: "We observed 3 dogs who had survived the shock suddenly expire the next day when they were again placed upon the animal table. We do not know how great a role this factor plays in our experiments." Cruelty to animals is a penal offense in all fifty of the United States. It is difficult to imagine that science will always be exempt if it continues to employ such methods. For an experiment of this type represents not only cruelty to life and disrespect for life: it is also its direct profanation.

However, it is an extreme example, having little in common with innumerable animal experiments, often involving vivisection, which are carried out in the absence of pain and terror. Yet man's newly acquired sense of humaneness has not yet rid modern society of its contention that all the results acquired by medical science will eventually contribute to the improvement of man's state. This contention is false and is based upon false premises: scientific research of the kind described above does not lead to an improvement of man's state. It leads to its direct retrogression. To acquiesce weakly in such inhumane experiments in the belief that they are necessary and must continue only emphasizes an inhumanity in ourselves. These experiments are not necessary. What is necessary is that man, collectively and individually, evolve by becoming as human as he is able.

Medical scientists, believing that the alleviation of human suffering is sufficient justification for all of their past actions and all of their future intentions, are naturally impatient of any external restrictions. It is quite understandable that they resent any efforts to curtail their freedom of action, especially when they are quite rightly convinced that the goal of their endeavors is essentially humane and idealistic. This view has been put forward very ably by Ingle in forthright discussions of the care and treatment of laboratory animals and the pertinent legislation pending before the United States Congress.[6] However, various facets of this question need increased illumination, and one of them concerns the statement that ". . . no one other than medical scientists should decide what experiments should or should not be done." While I wholeheartedly agree with this statement, I disagree with its implication. For it implies that medical scientists, regarding the concept of "necessary pain" as a scientific prerogative, impatiently say to the rest of mankind, "We know best what is good for you, so don't bother us but let us continue in our own way!" This attitude, it seems to me, expresses the failure of modern biology and medical science to recognize that man's increasing awareness of humaneness indicates that he has reached a new threshold in his evolution and that therefore the problem of painful animal experimentation now concerns all mankind and not just a panel of experts. If biologists and medical scientists would recognize this fact, they might find it advisable to adjust their activity to harmonize with current ideas concerning human progress. These ideas relate to the importance of human potentialities in all fields of endeavor—science being no exception.

With regard to the specific problem of animal experimentation, consider what is being written today in Sweden:

To reap for one's own benefit advantages through means which involve suffering and fear in defenseless living creatures must be felt to be a heavy burden of guilt for any humanely disposed person. No one can neglect the question, "With what right do we do this, we, who call ourselves human beings?" Herewith the problem is extended from the purely scientific plane to the ethical and the universal and becomes a problem which every man not only has the right but the duty to consider.[7]

And likewise in Denmark:

It shall be our hope and our endeavor that within physio-logical-medical research—as is, moreover, already happening —new methods will gradually be employed until finally it will not be permitted to employ higher animals as objects of oper-ations which cause a high degree of pain or suffering, a practice which is regarded by a growing circle of people in widely separated fields as ethically indefensible and therefore inadmissible.[8]

Such views are common today in animal welfare circles, and I believe that they are destined to receive much wider support.

The Problem of Restrictive Legislation

Today many persons outside the scientific profession feel that the best solution to the problem of painful animal experimentation is to restrict its practice by law. Such a view has long persisted. In a lengthy article on vivisection written more than fifty years ago for the *Encyclopaedia Britannica,* this statement appears: "It would be possible for cruelty of an unnecessary kind to result if the practice of vivisection were unrestricted." The author, himself a staunch supporter of vivisection, nevertheless felt that scientists needed external restriction in its practice. A more direct admis-sion of the human failings of scientists and the inadequacy of their objective humaneness could hardly be expressed.

Personally, I do not believe that external restriction, however much it has contributed to the prevention of animal cruelty in the past, will ever solve the present problem satisfactorily, nor that such legislation as is pending or contemplated today is worthy of wholehearted support. It is a superficial attack that fails to go to the heart of the matter. *For further restrictive legislation would only prevent many scientists from doing what they now earnestly desire to do.* In other words, it can prevent animal suffering, but it can never make anyone more human. That must come from within. And when it comes, scientific inhumaneness will no longer exist and legislation will be superfluous. It is not external restriction that is needed, it is self-restriction.

Of course, the final decisions as to what experiments should be performed must be made by scientists alone without outside interference. Anything else would be intolerable and degrading to the profession. Yet, surely, any profession which is in danger of being forced by public opinion to seek federal or state approval of its research plans lest it be otherwise guilty of inhumaneness needs to take serious stock of itself, its motives, and its means.*

One of the prime justifications of animal welfare societies is, I think, to continue to bring to the attention of the general public the facts available in scientific journals concerning the types of experiments which are today being carried out on animals. The pending legislation in America restricting animal experimentation already indicates which way the wind is blowing. Regardless of the outcome, there may also come a day when world opinion is sufficiently aroused by knowledge of the methods biologists and medical scientists employ to say simply to them, "We do not wish you to continue!"

If this ever is said, science will be forced to take heed; it flourishes, after all, only by the grace of modern society. The excessive interest, support, and good will it now enjoys is not necessarily everlasting. It is not at all difficult to envisage the day when mankind will refuse to tolerate for "its own good" the inhumaneness—and therefore the lack of humanness—of science.

---

* This might well include facing the fact that the driving force of biology and medical science is not unalloyed idealism but a complex of factors, including prestige, publication, professional advancement, grants, and business interests.

If the idealism of modern society and the idealism of modern science are ever to come to terms, a renewal of the scientific outlook will be much more necessary than restrictive legislation. Such a renewal would involve the emergence of the scientist's human potentialities and his realization that they are more precious to himself and to mankind than the attainment of new scientific knowledge. The objective humaneness of biological and medical research would thereby be supplemented by a subjective humaneness that would base animal experimentation first upon ethical considerations and second upon the discovery of new intellectual truths.

Modern Science and Human Evolution

It may be objected that both biology and medicine are already directing their attention to the ethical aspects of their activity. Consider, for example, the Universities Federation for Animal Welfare in Britain and the American Animal Care Panel. Consider these recent statements of a physiologist:

> We need further debate among scientists as to what kind of experiments which cause discomfort are necessary. Just as the ethical practices of medicine require repeated group discussion and review, so should the ethical aspects of animal experimentation be frequently examined by informed thinking within scientific groups . . . ,[9]
> . . . there are areas of research in which the ethics of certain experiments should be openly debated. I am thinking now of studies done on pain itself and severely painful injuries without anesthesia. I am not convinced that all such studies are necessary, but then these represent areas of research in which I am not competent.[10]

In the face of such evidence is there, then, need for words of alarm or criticism from an outsider? I think there is. While all of the above quotations except the last clause represent to me enlightened scientific thinking worthy of the highest praise, it is not at all certain—to judge from current scientific literature—that such views are widespread. It is even less certain that medical scientists and biologists are generally aware that the specific problem of painful animal experimentation is only a small part of the much greater problem of the role of modern science in human evolution, a fact that should form the natural basis for any discussion of the ethics of biological and medical research. For scientific progress today is an intellectual obsession that threatens to become uncontrollable unless scientists themselves exercise some self-restraint in its pursuit. Unchecked, it will lead straight to a scientifically directed world in which the intellect so dominates the spirit that man will no longer be interested in becoming more human.

Already the so-called benefits of scientific research are all too often based upon an utter disregard of human potentialities. Consider our desire to reach the moon, to explore outer space, to establish sperm and egg banks, to produce artificially a race of supermen, to make spring silent, and to direct our mental activities through the use of drugs. Humanly speaking, the attainment of such "benefits" is only misdirected energy. And even if the benefit be a truly human desire, such as the improvement of man's health, then it must be attained only by means that are compatible with our ultimate goal, that of becoming more human. If the means violate this goal, the benefit attained, however splendid it may appear, will also be tarnished. It cannot be otherwise. The ends never justify the means.

But let us be more specific. Medical science, inspired by objective humaneness, considers it a duty to do all in its power to prevent disease, to prolong human life, and to alleviate human suffering; it has already come very far in the attainment of these worthy ends. If, through increased knowledge, it could elucidate the etiology and improve the treatment of many of the now prevalent human afflictions, mankind would be still more benefited—provided that the means caused no repression of the human potentialities of those who employed them. But, one might protest, suppose the causes and treatments of these maladies could not be elucidated without the prior infliction of animal suffering: does not man come first? Of course he does. That's just the point. *We will never know how unique we really are until we begin to act as humanly as we are able.* Yet medical science, in looking forward to the day when it shall no longer be necessary for human beings to endure suffering, seems to believe more strongly than ever that inhumane methods are justifiable, for it is now engaged in an all-out attack upon pain itself. Experimental animals are being subjected to revoltingly painful investigations, because animal suffering is considered necessary to make human suffering unnecessary. Such a scientific outlook, I think, typifies the objective humaneness of medical research in its failure to understand the basic issues at stake. These involve not so much the desirability of maintaining man in a state of perpetual good health as the desirability of his being able to attain a state of increased humanness.

Those scientists who are discontent with our present state of wisdom and desire to continue their investigations of pain by the further torture of animals might reflect upon the ultimate goal of their endeavors. Suppose that science should one day become so exceedingly wise that it could abolish human pain. Would man thereby automatically become more human because he need not endure pain? I think not. Nor do I think that anyone ever became more human by swallowing a pain-relieving pill. A medical profession which triumphantly produces tranquilizing drugs for the happiness of mankind has no more understanding of the human potential than a society that becomes increasingly dependent upon them as necessary aids to a better life. It must be remembered that a blissful human life devoid of physical or mental suffering would be no whole life at all. In contrast to animals, our lives involve a spiritual development requiring the experience of suffering so that we can exhibit the courage which is a part of our unique humanness.

These words are not meant in any way to imply that the desire for further improvement of man's health is unnecessary, but only to stimulate thought about the ultimate consequences of realizing this goal and to express the view that it is unnecessary to employ the compulsion, the haste, and the means which are now rampant in medical science and biology. Scientific research has always proceeded as though the attainment of its goal was more important than the humanness of those who pursue it. Today medical and biological scientists believe, with a fanaticism that matches the fanaticism of the anti-vivisectionists whom they find it convenient to scorn, that the alleviation of human suffering must be attained by all available means. Already we have medical knowledge and medicinal preparations in abundance for the prevention and relief of pain. Much of this knowledge was obtained and many of these medicines were produced at the cost of a great deal of animal suffering, and possessing them, we shall naturally employ them, regardless of how they were obtained. But this is no justification whatever for extending our knowledge or continuing the production of new and better preparations by the inhumane methods of the past and the present—for it is time we knew better.

It has been suggested earlier that within the field of biology there is need of a renewal in biological thinking which would be primarily based upon self-restraint and which has been called "biological sophrosyne." That such a renewal would necessarily lead to that greatest of all contemporary heresies, the retardation of scientific progress, would, it seems to me, only be a desirable corollary. In this Scientific Age we all have need of more self-restraint, and modern society together with modern science could do no better than to stop to consider the benefits that are expected to follow from continued intellectual achievements at all costs, and then to decide whether this goal is promoting or preventing human progress.

In a thought-provoking contribution to the current debate on science versus humanism, Charles Davy characterized the present scientific outlook as an "onlooker consciousness," which he considers to represent only a temporary phase in human history.[11] The relevance of this view to the present discussion lies in Davy's belief that man's "responsive awareness" of the universe is destined to evolve still further. If man is to become as human as he is able, such an evolutionary development seems to be required, and man's growing awareness of humaneness already indicates that he has attained a new evolutionary threshold. Yet it seems improbable that he will get beyond it as long as he accepts the modern scientific outlook that human suffering must be reduced through the rapid attainment of new scientific truths by all available means. This outlook only whets his appetite for the unending stream of new practical applications accruing from scientific research and increases his delusion that human progress is dependent upon unrestricted scientific progress. But there is all reason to hope that he will advance beyond his present threshold when his consciousness reveals to him that it is a virtue to endure suffering and a vice to inflict it and that its alleviation must progress no further than humane means allow.

Who knows, perhaps such an awareness of knowing when it is fitting to stop might provide us with the everlasting existence of that pain and suffering which is necessary to bring out the best within us and to ensure, both individually and collectively, that our future progress be truly human after all?

IV

Superior Knowledge, Modern Science, and the Human Potential

He that teacheth man knowledge, shall not he know?
—94th Psalm.

Polanyi's Concept of Superior Knowledge and Ultra-Biology

The appearance in 1958 of Michael Polanyi's *Personal Knowledge*[1] offered to the Scientific Age an impressive concept of the ultimate nature and justification of scientific knowledge. Scientists, we were told, are laboring under a delusion in maintaining that their business is the strictly detached acquisition of truth. On the contrary, the responsible scientist's attainment of knowledge of objective reality is no mere impersonal and passive experience, but a personal commitment by which he acts not as he pleases but rather as he must. Scientific knowledge is, in fact, a union of the objective with the personal; it rests ultimately upon belief, and it reveals a new vision of reality, which is attained only in the most personal way through indispensable intellectual passions.

Detached scientific objectivity, on the other hand, is a delusion that threatens not only science itself but other human activities as well, and which automatically impoverishes our moral standards. If modern scientists would acknowledge their personal commitment to the search for truth, their intentions could partake of universality, and they could "restore science to the great family of human aspirations, by which men hope to fulfill the purpose of their existence as thinking beings."[2] It is evident that Polanyi's own personal commitment to seek the truth and state his findings was the moral compulsion which led him to disclose what he believed to be the false and dangerous ideal of scientific objectivity; it follows that however one responds to his beliefs, one cannot fail to admire a man who so desired to live his own words that he spent nearly a decade in doing so.

One particular theme in *Personal Knowledge* bears so directly upon human progress that it calls for reillumination through the most comprehensive scrutiny and appraisal. This is the concept of "superior knowledge," which Polanyi introduces by extending its domain far beyond the knowledge which science has given us. For him, superior knowledge embraces all aspects of human culture which a free, modern society accepts as most valuable. It is the record of the thoughts and deeds of the most enlightened men and women, living or dead, and constitutes a pattern of ideals to which every society adheres for guidance: it is the cultural tradition to which we are dedicated. And, continues Polanyi, to the superiority of these great men "we entrust ourselves, by trying to understand their works and to follow their teachings and examples." This doctrine, so significant for any contemplation of human evolution, is then referred back again to science through Polanyi's idea of "ultra-biology."

Ultra-biology, in brief, is simply biology's ultimate extrapolation: the biologist's study of great men. Far from constituting a mere cult of hero worship, it is in the mind of Polanyi a further extension of the advance of biology, in which personal commitment plays an increasingly important role. Here a subtle distinction is drawn between the participation of the biologist in the achievements of living beings lower than himself and in the achievements of human beings superior to himself. While in both types of biological study he is committed to the search for truth, in the former case he is not himself appreciably modified by the personal knowledge he attains. In the latter case, since his knowledge is "centering on things higher than himself," he is profoundly modified by its attainment. For by submitting to the superior knowledge of his masters, who are greater than himself, he acknowledges his own inferiority and is therefore committed to self-improvement by personal participation in the attainment of truth. Only when scientists are ready to discard as delusions the ideals of detached objectivity and elimination of belief and passion, and substitute for them the more human ideal of personal commitment in their search for truth, will they be able to justify their activity and to realize the role of ultra-biology in human evolution. According to Polanyi, herein lies the hope of a better world.

These are noble thoughts. So noble that they cannot, and should not, be evaluated by the cold, dispassionate method of objective scientific analysis alone. Rather, let me attempt to consider them more in the light of what I passionately believe them to be: the meta-scientific reflections of a superior mind that demand the most respectful attention.

No brief discussion could adequately do justice to all aspects of such a comprehensive theme as superior knowledge. Accordingly, it is my purpose to limit this chapter to the twentieth century's appraisal of its superior knowledge in the hope of persuading others that we are neglecting its most essential part and that such a way of life is inherently perilous.

Human Greatness

In considering the twentieth century's evaluation of its heritage, I will follow Polanyi in regarding our entire superior knowledge as synonymous with the thoughts and deeds of our greatest men.

But since in our day the concept of greatness is vague and impermanent, it will first be necessary to attempt to crystallize the meaning that human greatness has for me.

Our entire superior knowledge can be broadly divided into three principal categories: (1) science, (2) art, and (3) philosophy and religion. The first is chiefly concerned with objective truth; the second, with beauty; and the third, with virtue; but these compartments are by no means watertight. The scientific achievements of a Galileo, a Newton, a Darwin, or an Einstein are remarkable manifestations of the encounter of superior human intellects with objective reality, and in their attainment of truth they have, for the initiated, their own beauty. The noblest works of art and music are not conceived in order to ascertain the truth about the world around us but, I suppose, in order to enhance its beauty; yet in doing so, they so perfectly satisfy a basic human need that they must in some ineffable way be related to the truth. The most important manifestations of the third category partake directly of truth, beauty, and virtue as well, and thereby concern themselves with the most basic of human needs, ethics and morals. The human greatness which is common to all categories can thus be thought of as man's participation in varying degrees in truth, beauty, and goodness—values which I hold to be absolute and imperishable; therefore I believe that human greatness partakes of universality and endures. This oversimplified attempt at definition is, of course, in no way original, but it does provide the necessary foundation for the ideas to follow.

Transmission of Superior Knowledge

If, then, the superior knowledge of any society consists in the total contribution of its greatest men, it is at once evident that the remarkable intellectual achievements of the leading scientists of the last four hundred years have vastly increased the store of superior knowledge available to the twentieth century. But, as we have seen, scientific superior knowledge is only a part of the whole, and in recalling that the history of science represents only the last 6 percent of man's civilized life, we can grasp the enormous totality of human activity and accomplishments that preceded the Scientific Age. The different races that constitute the species *Homo sapiens* have walked the face of the earth for some fifty thousand years, and six thousand years ago the first civilizations were emerging from the Neolithic cultures of the Mediterranean area. Upon this continuous accumulation and selection of human experience and insight is based our cultural tradition, upon which, in turn, are based our religious, political, and social institutions. While succeeding ages have attempted to improve man's state by reinterpreting, re-evaluating, and modifying these traditions, they have retained a feeling of respect for the non-scientific superior knowledge embodied in them—a respect often augmented by compulsion and force, since societies in the past were far less free than they are now. As a result, superior knowledge has been transmitted more or less intact down through the ages, constituting what Sir Julian Huxley characterized as the "psychosocial" phase of human evolution[3]—a slow, cumulative cultural transmission which has supplemented biological evolution and which only in recent times has become increasingly rapid. In this sense, one can envisage society as having been guided and directed by its respect for the human greatness of the past. Discontinuity has not been a part of human development.

Submission to Superior Knowledge

Yet Polanyi goes further in his concept of the guidance that societies have received from the superior knowledge of the past, believing that it involves not only respect, but submission and dedication as well. Speaking of great men, he writes: "For it is not to their person, but to what we understand to be their teaching, that we pledge ourselves," and, further, that ". . . human greatness can be recognized only by submission to it. . . ." But even when he qualifies this view by considering human greatness as belonging "to the family of things which exist only for those committed to them," I do not think his concept of the relation of man to his superior knowledge expresses the whole truth. I would add that man's professed self-dedication to the greatness of his heritage has for the most part been self-deception, if not hypocrisy. With the exception of the few enlightened minds, submission to superior knowledge by both the educated and the non-educated has been compulsory or automatic and unreflecting. Most men, it is true, have submitted, but without ever having known emotional dedication. For, surely, if all men had submitted to human greatness by passionate commitment and participation, all men would have been great!

Probably the closest approach to mass participation in superior knowledge was the behavior of the Christian martyrs; their lofty idealism was, however, based upon their dedication to the superior knowledge of one Mind alone and their concomitant denial of much or all of the greatness of the pagan world. Their gaze was fixed on a life in heaven, and while this faith led them to face death with unsurpassed courage and unbelievable joy, their devaluation of life on earth prevented them from realizing their whole human potential. Only the rarest individuals in each age have known that the attainment of the humanness of which they are capable requires first an intense preoccupation with the sum total of human greatness that preceded them.

When we come to the Scientific Age—this period of explosive advances in all branches of learning and the accompanying extension of what Teilhard de Chardin has called the "noosphere"[4]— we find that failure to submit to our entire superior knowledge is more widespread than ever before. Curiously, the knowledge of the history of the organic and inorganic world that we at the same time are so rapidly amassing points to a greater interest in the past than any preceding age has ever shown. Let us examine this seeming paradox.

Current Attitudes Toward the Past

For several decades an army of specialists has been engaged in studying the past with all the customary means and fervor of modern science. The results of all this organized activity can be seen in any large city, where the windows of the book stores abound with superbly produced books on archaeology, anthropology, ethnology, history, and evolution. Many authors outside the field of science have also extended our knowledge of the past with sumptuous works depicting in natural color the ancient art collections of the world's museums and the sites of ancient civilizations, while musicologists have made available on phonograph records the highlights of the whole history of music from ancient Greece to the recent past. Such contributions follow one upon another with overwhelming rapidity. That such a large market exists for them can only mark a growing world-wide interest in the past. Certainly, one might say, we are not neglecting our heritage! I am sure that we are.

In the first place, much of this new knowledge of the past is not superior knowledge at all, if, as Polanyi rightly maintains, the superior knowledge of a society is primarily "what its classics have uttered and its heroes and saints have done." That which catches the eye and tempts the purse in the book shops is beautiful, informative, and extraordinarily interesting, but most of it is irrelevant in combating present evils or in conceiving a better world. It appears to be primarily based upon satisfying our natural curiosity as to the way of life of our ancestors and the appearance of their world; while contributing to an elucidation of our origins and making available for our appreciation the physical beauty of the past, much of it is merely the elegant compilation and description of the specialist. One sometimes wonders whether all the time and energy that the book world now directs toward technological excellence could not be better applied.

Of course, there are many contemporary authors who are able to recognize the essential superior knowledge of the past. Admirable studies and interpretations of various aspects of the sociology, language, literature, religion, and philosophy of the past continue to appear, together with newly edited literary masterpieces of the past, and frequent performances of the highpoints of its musical and dramatic art. Yet even these appraisals of superior knowledge appear to be inadequate, for they fail to excite anyone concerned into submission and commitment. The last fifty years have given no indication that all this accumulated knowledge of the past has caused the slightest improvement in human behavior. Perhaps those classical scholars who spend their days writing of ancient spiritual beauty themselves lead lives of greater moral excellence than other men, but I am not aware that this is generally true.

The spiritual significance of the past does not seem to have penetrated man's consciousness. Although he has become aware of the concept of humaneness, his amorality or immorality is revealed in countless ways. An international awareness of modern evils makes their existence no less shameful, especially in view of the silence of most scholars whose business it is to know of the moral greatness of the past, the sporadic and ineffectual protests of the official spokesmen of the great religions, and the generally prevailing contentment with the Scientific Age and the material well-being of a welfare state. To the essence of the past—to those greatest thoughts and deeds of which men have been capable—our age is no more dedicated than any preceding age has been.

What characterizes our age is not, however, only a passive or superficial interest in the past, or even the failure to recognize this state of affairs. An active and contemptuous dislike prevails as well. The vehement refusal of so many contemporary men and women to be guided by their heritage is potently revealed in the absurdity and nihilism of contemporary art, literature, and music. An absolute negation of traditional values is the keynote of the

Weltbild of thousands and thousands of individuals today who find the keenest pleasure in "anti-culture" of all kinds. Even contemporary philosophers derive much satisfaction from their attempt to prove how meaningless were the contributions of their predecessors. And as such expressions of distaste for the greatness of the past continue to enjoy public interest and support, it can be assumed that an ever increasing number of twentieth-century men are uninterested in resisting the overthrow of so much of their intellectual, spiritual, and aesthetic tradition.

The Influence of the Scientific Outlook Upon the Idea of Human Progress

Both these trends of passive interest in the past and contemptuous denial of its greatness are, I believe, explainable by the fact that ours is a Scientific Age with a new set of standards and ideals different from any previous age—including the standard of human greatness. Our present faith is centered not upon the sum total of our spiritual values but solely upon those new truths which are revealed by intellectual progress; and as the world outlook is dominated by the scientific outlook, modern man places most of his faith in innovation. This is equivalent to saying that the superior knowledge to which he submits is primarily that of science alone. It follows that submission and participation in the superior knowledge of the Pre-Scientific World is no more a part of the outlook of those who are now engaged in studying the past than of those cultural avant-gardists who see past and present life only as an absurdity. One of the dominant themes of *Personal Knowledge* is that the false ideal of scientific objectivity impoverishes human morals; yet modern scientism is much more than objectivity, false or otherwise: it is also the cult of novelty and blind faith in the compulsion of intellectual progress—and it already appears that the scientists' dedication to such ideals is more disastrous to morality than Polanyi seemed to be aware.

Scientism has indoctrinated modern society in the belief that only the New is valuable and that scientific progress is therefore synonymous with human progress. Accordingly, many take it for granted that only the emanations of contemporary minds, or at least minds from the recent past, have anything of value for them. But so permeated are such individuals with belief in the desirability of change that they do not submit to those contemporary minds which are awake to the dangers of scientism—to Polanyi,[5] Mumford,[6] Eiseley,[7] to Walshe,[8] Farrington,[9] and Heitler.[10] Most persons prefer to submit to the superior knowledge emanating from the minds of those scientific leaders who preach scientific innovation. Outside the realm of science, even age and experience count for little. Thus, in a recent Copenhagen newspaper interview a Danish astronomer and authority on electronic computers expressed the view that the *Weltanschauung* which is being derived from modern calculating machines opens such tremendously novel perspectives that no one over thirty-five years of age can ever hope to adjust his way of thinking even to comprehend it. The implication is clear: older persons might just as well keep their thoughts to themselves. It is perhaps worth adding that at the time of the interview the scientist in question was himself just thirty-five.

An oft-repeated question today is this: "How can the world visions of the most enlightened minds of the past be other than hopelessly antiquated when science is so rapidly changing the world?" That durable values might be the essence of our heritage is apparently not worth anyone's consideration in a world whose standard of human greatness is the ability to bring forth something new. Science keeps drumming into the world consciousness the notion that innovation is, after all, the supreme panacea, for the more new facts discovered and the greater our knowledge of objective reality, then the truer are our visions of the universe and man's place in it, and the better we can guide our future development. *Ergo*, any attempt to restrain scientific progress would be nothing short of madness. With both intellect and emotion let us consider this point of view: nothing less will suffice.

Contemporary Scientific Visions of the Future

The world visions of contemporary scientists are based upon scientific knowledge of objective reality and are therefore necessarily different from the world visions of the past. Polanyi contends that although science has always prided itself on its preoccupation with objectivity and its neglect of subjectivity, the most significant visions are actually based upon indispensable intellectual passions and personal commitment to the search for truth. This, I am sure, is true—and especially today; leading men of science, knowing more about objective reality than ever before, leave behind the dispassionate objectivity of their profession in copiously bestowing upon modern man their visions and proposals for his improvement. I cannot, however, agree with Polanyi's further contention that personal and passionate commitment to knowledge of objective reality automatically ensures that the scientific visions arising from it are humanly desirable. For although these scientific leaders earnestly believe that they speak for the good of humanity and that their intentions thereby partake of universality, their proposals for a better world actually represent no more than the outlook of a small group of men of one particular generation and culture whose dedication to superior knowledge is limited to that of science alone. And with what right, one might ask, can one so dogmatically conclude that contemporary scientists, who are personally and passionately committed to the truth, are at the same time scorning the superior knowledge of the Pre-Scientific World? I think it is easy to demonstrate that this is just what they are doing; contemporary biologists—those scientists whose business it is to know about life—so little believe in the greatness of which human life has been capable that they are arrogantly proposing its permanent and irrevocable alteration.

Biologists would probably retort that they most certainly do recognize past human greatness but are so dissatisfied with the slowness with which it appears that they wish to hurry it along and, if possible, to augment it on the way. The fallaciousness of this argument can, I think, also be demonstrated.

Consider first that the practical applications of scientific advances have already been responsible for various indirect and accidental alterations in our world. One need only be reminded of *Silent Spring*.[11] Worse changes may be in store. Sir Bernard Lovell's recent warning about the consequences of continued space research was based upon the unexplained relationship existing between mental disturbances and magnetic storms, and the possibility that one of the causes of the latter are nuclear explosions. From another field, experiments on animals have revealed that their emotional state can be radically altered following brain surgery. These are highly disquieting thoughts, but they are less disquieting than the planned alterations already envisaged by scientists. Having genetic, chemical, and medical knowledge sufficient to direct the further development of the human race, eugenists are now proposing the establishment of sperm and egg banks for the controlled production of a race of superior men, and psychologists are advocating the pharmacological control of human behavior. It is evident that all of these scientists with visions passionately believe they can improve upon nature: it is characteristic of them to speak so hopefully and so vaguely about intellectual and moral progress and the future greatness of man.

Yet of his past greatness they speak not at all. They dwell often enough upon human evolution, but in their pride and their haste they forget the human greatness of the past—that supreme excellence of which man has been capable and which the Greeks recognized and called *arete*—they forget that this is our only touchstone of humanness, and only through personal knowledge of it can we know what it means to be a human being. They desire to alter man's body and mind in order to "improve" the human race, but they have made no attempt to define human-ness. Although they acknowledge no masters, they have failed, as far as I can see, to demonstrate that their own humanness is of a superior order and have therefore not yet indicated what stand-ard, other than that of science, they would employ in producing superior men. The greatness of the past—this yardstick which is staring them in the face—they do not see, for they have eyes only for future innovation. Submitting to the undeniable greatness of scientific superior knowledge, they are unaware that biology—or ultra-biology, as Polanyi would say—includes a submission to the greatness of men who had no scientific knowledge whatever. Let us never forget the truism that human greatness in the Pre-Scien-tific World emerged in the complete absence of science.

A direct outcome of the new perspectives and visions opened up by scientific intelligence is the automation of knowledge, the dangers of which Mumford has so trenchantly exposed,[12] to-gether with the hope of a world directed by science. We read, for example, in the proceedings of a recent symposium of biologists on man and his future (in which Polanyi's work is not even mentioned) the following view expressed by an historian of sci-ence:

> Part of the business of the transition to a Big Science phase is that scientists are becoming very much more numerous and are becoming immensely more powerful and prestigeous [sic] . . . many scientists actually have their hands on the controls of political action. This is happening within the present gen-eration and is one of the most optimistic things about the future of man.[13]

And if, through a fervent desire for an accelerated rate of scientific advance, even the most enlightened men of science are committed to only a part of the superior knowledge at their dis-posal, what of the great majority of less gifted scientists whose ability does not qualify them to rank as leaders of their profes-sion? I refer to those whom Aldous Huxley termed the "intellec-tual proletariat of science" and about whom he quoted a con-temporary scientist as saying, " 'A large number of young people take up scientific research as a career these days, but regrettably few are impelled into it by a passionate curiosity as to the secrets of nature. For the vast majority it is a job, like any other job. . . .' "[14] This proletariat, whose labors keep science flourishing, spend professional lives accumulating objective facts for the sake of salary, publication, and prestige. Without even knowing commitment or intellectual passion, they can only passively submit to the visions and proposals of their leaders and by their very number intensify the world-wide delusion that science can give us the truest vision of man's place in the universe and that a scientifically directed world is as desirable as it is inevitable.

The Dehumanizing Aspects of a Scientifically Directed World

To desire a scientifically directed world seems, for the following reasons, to indicate a failure to understand the human potential:

(1) Without first having submitted to the greatness of the entire superior knowledge at their disposal, scientists have no standard of humanness and thus lack adequate knowledge of that which they desire to shape, alter, and direct.

(2) The means by which they would improve the human race is the superior knowledge of science, which, being knowledge of objective reality, is in itself devoid of morality; therefore any moral effect their efforts might have upon human conduct would be accidental, unpredictable, and meaningless.

(3) A scientific explanation of the essence of human greatness does not exist; no amount of genetic, psychological, chemical, or medical knowledge available today can explain virtue and goodness. It follows that although science possesses the means to direct the further development of man by controlling his propagation, improving his health, and possibly raising his intelligence, it has no means whatever for augmenting his essential humanness.

I believe, further, that to consider a scientifically directed world as inevitable indicates a failure to understand the full significance of the present stage of psychosocial evolution. For contemporary scientific visions are all characterized by a passionate belief in human intelligence and a condescending interest in human virtue—and this is to put the cart before the horse. In scientific circles—and far beyond them—it is tacitly agreed that science *must* attempt to improve the human race because scientific knowledge and its utilization represents the inevitable and predestined course of life in the universe and the unfolding of the human personality: the realization of the human potential necessarily embraces the free exercise of man's intellect.

This point of view completely neglects the fact that the realization of the human potential also includes the exercise of moral restraint and moderation—that which two thousand years ago was called sophrosyne and was recognized as an essential part of human greatness. Let science advance, certainly—for it is a most worthy and admirable endeavor to discover the truth about objective reality—but let it advance slowly and humbly and in full awareness of its proper place in the general scheme of things. For scientific sophrosyne means neither obscurantism nor a passive, indifferent holding back from the truth. It means a taut, disciplined restraint, intoxicating its possessor by imparting to him the knowledge that his choice is making him more human.

The passionate interest of the enlightened scientist in the attainment of scientific knowledge is based upon his discovery of new truths of objective reality; the passionate interest of the layman in scientific progress is based upon its practical application. In neither case is the emotion evoked of prime significance in human progress. If this passion were to be transferred to the world of the spirit—that world wherein is to be found the real stuff of human greatness—it would be transformed into love, and we would at last be able to contemplate man's future without the slightest trace of fear.

The Human Significance of the Psychosocial
Stage of Evolution

Here, it seems to me, we touch upon the deeper significance of psychosocial evolution: man has finally reached a stage of his history where he has attained more education and more freedom than ever before, and these blessings are meant to be utilized in his further ascent: education in order to know what it means to be a human being, and freedom in order to choose to become as human as he is able. Yet the choice is not between a scientifically directed world or a cessation of scientific advance. The choice is between being passively carried along by the surging tide of scientific progress and innovation, amassing without end scientific knowledge, and allowing our waxing noosphere to dictate man's future, or passionately desiring a world in which the goal of each human life is to realize its potential by striving toward immortality through participation in human greatness. But without education imparting to us a knowledge of past human *arete*, we can never identify ourselves with it, and in the absence of a goal, the latent magnificence in each one of us is doomed to waste away, unnoticed.

Hear now the thoughts of a contemporary biologist. "Eugenics and euphenics are the biological counterparts of education, a panacea that has a longer but equally contentious tradition. The troubled history of Utopian education warns us to take care in rebuilding human personality on infirm philosophy."[15] To call infirm the philosophy of the past, that expression *par excellence* of human greatness, and to be unchallenged in doing so, is to reveal how few are sufficiently awake to know that man's progress depends upon his submission to that which he now neglects.

But, fortunately, those who are awake express their thoughts, too:

. . . decisions of critical importance to the human race are being taken today on the basis of ten-year-old knowledge, confidently applied by highly disciplined specialists who too often display the shortcomings of ten-year-old minds, for they regard as a special merit their deliberate practice of cutting their minds off from ten thousand years of human experience and culture. . . . Strangely, they have not even a suspicion that the vast quantity of exact knowledge now at our disposal is no guarantee whatever of our having sufficient emotional sensitiveness and moral insight to make good use of it; if anything, the exact contrary has already proved true.[16]

Recapitulation of the Arguments

In summary, let me briefly recapitulate the arguments put forth above:

The great majority of men, while recognizing the enduring character of their entire superior knowledge, has submitted to it passively or by compulsion. Now, when societies are more free than ever before, most men neglect it still further, preferring to listen to the visions and proposals of contemporary leaders of science, and caring not that the superior knowledge of objective reality is the least essential part of the knowledge at our disposal. Yet they should care: for even if scientific visions are rid of false objectivity and based upon personal commitment to the truth, a scientifically dominated world can never diminish the appalling disproportion which now exists between intelligence and virtue. As long as men of science continue to neglect the most valuable part of their superior knowledge, their visions of reality, however passionately they believe in them, will be inadequate and their proposals to direct man's future, dangerous. Their desire to utilize their knowledge to alter man's nature has already demonstrated their dissatisfaction with existing human greatness—and thereby their lack of understanding of the human potential.

Of surpassing importance for our age, it seems to me, is a goal quite different from the obsessive belief in the desirability and inevitability of a waxing "noosphere," even if it be attained by ridding science of false objectivity. It must rather be an equally compelling belief that the moral and spiritual greatness embodied in the superior knowledge of our heritage is indispensable for present and future man. Such a belief may be considered as a kind of ultra-biology and may be thought of as a future extension of biology in which life reflects upon itself and submission to human greatness necessarily takes place. I would prefer to say that it is a faith which can already be entertained, for it requires no further scientific standards or knowledge whatever, either of man or of the universe. It involves simply a love of the enduring values of our spiritual heritage, which already are the precious, yet largely unrecognized, possessions of each one of us.

V

Nightingales, Hawks, and the Two Cultures

From the love of the beautiful has sprung all good to gods and men.

—*Plato*, The Symposium, *197b.*

Representative Views of the Relation between Science and the Humanities

For the past five years the English-speaking world has been vigorously debating Sir Charles Snow's concept of the "two cultures,"[1] in which he deplored the incompatibility between the outlook of men of science and men of letters. Although the magnitude of the response, which has ranged from wholehearted agreement to stout denial of the existence of two cultures and even violent personal abuse, may be due to the peculiar qualifications of an author who stands with a foot in each camp, the problem has been recognized and debated since the eighteenth century.

Some of the best minds have openly professed an obscurantist enmity to scientific progress out of fear that their poetic vision would be impaired by increasing factual knowledge of the external world. Other equally gifted men, including, of course, those professional scientists who cared to reflect upon the matter, have welcomed all new intellectual advances and their practical applications, being convinced that human progress cannot be retarded and hopefully pointing out that, for the sake of man's wholeness, the gap between science and the humanities must somehow be bridged. Indeed, many literary men have long looked forward to the increase of scientific knowledge as an ever expanding source of rich, usable material. Such an outlook has in no way been exclusively European: in a study of American literature and culture, which was written in the 1920s and which Santayana called "the best book about America that I have read," we find:

> In America, it was easy for an Emerson or a Whitman to see the importance of welding together the interests which science represented, and those which, through the accidents of its historic development, science denied. Turning from a limited European past to a wider heritage, guiding themselves by all the reports of their own day, these poets continued the old voyage of exploration on the plane of the mind, and, seeking passage to India, found themselves coasting along strange shores. None of the fine minds of the Golden Day was afraid to welcome the new forces that were at large in the world. Need I recall that Whitman wrote an apostrophe to the locomotive, that Emerson said a steamship sailing promptly between America and Europe might be as beautiful as a star, and that Thoreau, who loved to hear the wind in the pine needles, listened with equal pleasure to the music of the telegraph wires? That practical instrumentalities were to be worshiped, never occurred to these writers: but that they added a new and significant element to our culture, which the poet was ready to absorb and include in his report upon the universe, was profoundly true. . . . These perceptions called, of course, for great works of the imagination; for in proportion as intelligence was dealing more effectually with the instrumentalities of life, it became more necessary for the imagination to project more complete and satisfying ends. . . . None of these men was caught by the dominant abstractions: each saw life whole, and sought a whole life.[2]

These sentiments were valid in the nineteenth century. They were equally valid when they were written. But the "forces that were at large in the world" in the 1920s have now become so omnipotent and threatening that I believe both the present and the future validity of these words is questionable. To develop this point of view will be the chief concern of this chapter. Let me begin by considering some representative samples of the current debate on the two cultures.

In the first place, Snow regrets the fact that many contemporary men of letters are indifferent or antagonistic to scientific progress. His regret is not so much concerned with their failure to utilize all the new wealth science is placing at their disposal, but rather with their failure to recognize that since the application of science can ameliorate the unnecessary suffering of the majority of mankind, science in itself is an undeniable good which should be welcomed. Concerning the aid which science can give to the unfortunate, he writes: "All this we *know* how to do. It does not require one additional scientific discovery, though new scientific discoveries must help us. It depends on the spread of the scientific revolution all over the world." At the same time he welcomes, as the best means of spreading this revolution, a rapid increase in the number of trained scientists and therefore the unimpeded advance of scientific knowledge. Snow's enthusiasm for scientific progress thus stems from his concern for those people whose survival is threatened from lack of the "primal things."

Yet he is interested in more than mere quantitative increase in numbers of human beings. He also regrets that our humanitarian responsibilities to those who live in unindustrialized countries are at present primarily the sole concern of the scientists, for the latter, he believes, are unable to do their best job so long as they continue to regard our traditional culture, that which has long been the life blood of the literary man, as irrelevant to their activities. He desires, therefore, that through a renewal of our educational system, the existent hostility between science and literature be replaced by an amalgamation leading to a superior third culture based upon the "human effects of the scientific revolution." This proposal for increased communication and cooperation between literature and science for the benefit of all concerned—the needy, the sick, and the ignorant as well as the affluent, the healthy, and the wise—denotes a genuine interest in augmenting the individual wholeness of all men. In brief, Snow's philanthropic approach to the problem associated with the two cultures is such a profoundly decent attempt to eradicate much of the unnecessary misery of contemporary life that it can only be applauded. Yet his altruism must not obscure other equally important aspects of the problem.

Davy also envisages a future third culture.[3] Like Snow, he would in no way limit or obstruct scientific progress, for he considers that the modern scientific outlook is a "necessary and a potentially beneficial stage in human evolution." While he also regards the modern scientific *Weltbild* as far from satisfying, his vision penetrates deeper into the heart of the matter than Snow's. Davy's third culture is not based upon continued scientific progress and the "solid unquestionable reality" of the world. Rather, it is based upon enhanced levels of human consciousness, which he sees as a necessary accompaniment of human evolution.

Yudkin challenges Snow's views, maintaining that the rapid expansion of scientific education in order to produce more scientists and more scientific knowledge is incompatible with a dual system of education based upon science and traditional culture.[4] Nor does he believe that the work of the man of letters would be substantially improved by his assimilating the results of scientific progress. He offers some sparse, yet valuable, comments on the desirability of the further acquisition of knowledge but sees little hope for future improvement in the mutual relationship between scientists and non-scientists and pessimistically concludes by expressing the fear that the traditional culture may soon give way to a single, all-embracing scientific culture.

Madge is more optimistic. In focusing attention upon the question whether the poetic and the scientific images of man can be reconciled, he does not share the view that art and literature are necessarily doomed to extinction. He suggests:

> What is perhaps needed above all is a philosophy or set of ideas which will give the artist and poet the same conviction of intrinsic value of their work as is possessed in almost super-abundant measure by the contemporary scientist. To create such a philosophy would in itself involve a transformation in the goals of modern society.[5]

In 1963, nearly four decades after Mumford's views about the two cultures were published, they were re-echoed and expanded by Aldous Huxley:

> To the twentieth century man of letters science offers a treasure of newly discovered facts and tentative hypotheses. If he accepts this gift and if, above all, he is sufficiently talented and resourceful to be able to transform the new materials into works of literary art, the twentieth century man of letters will be able to treat the age-old, and perennially relevant, theme of human destiny with a depth of understanding, a width of reference of which, before the rise of science, his predecessors (through no fault of their own, no defect of genius) were incapable. . . . To ignore [this new information] is an act of literary cowardice . . . let us advance together, men of letters and men of science, further and further into the ever expanding regions of the unknown.[6]

Such words as these are bound to stimulate further thought. It appears that despite *Brave New World Revisited*[7] and all the other eloquent manifestations of his recognition of the dangers of a scientifically directed world, Huxley did, in fact, share the prevailing belief of our Scientific Age that rapid scientific progress is inevitable. This belief, persisting unshaken for decades, seems to lie behind all the utterances of the current debate on the two cultures. It is based upon the assumption that evolution demands that human experience must be carried to the limits of man's intelligence and ingenuity. Teilhard de Chardin termed such an acceleration in human mental activity as "noogenesis," envisaging it as a kind of predestined evolutionary development.[8] The further expansion of our "noosphere" thus becomes both ineluctable and desirable. As a result, all advances in knowledge, if not indiscriminately welcomed, are everywhere accepted as tokens of man's increasing wholeness, which, according to many, is synonymous with his deeper understanding of reality, his increased ability to portray it in words, and his augmented power to direct his own destiny. Thus, since man, through self-compulsion, is rushing headlong forward to make the unknown known, any attempt to slacken his pace or redirect his course is dismissed as wishful thinking, reactionary obscurantism, or even cowardice.

In the fullness of time this twentieth-century *Weltanschauung* may turn out to be less enduring than is now supposed. Huxley attempted to demonstrate its permanent validity with a nightingale. Let us consider his words.

The Nightingale

Man's response to the peculiar quality of the nightingale's song was first recorded in Greek myths, and following Aristophanes and Ovid has been a fertile source of poetry ever since. No one recognized the intrinsic beauty and worth of these literary creations more than Aldous Huxley. Yet as a twentieth-century man of letters who knew more than his predecessors, these beloved works of art could no longer content him. Of the nightingale he wrote:

Philomel, it turns out, is not Philomel, but her mate. And when the cock-nightingale sings, it is not in pain, not in passion, not in ecstasy, but simply in order to proclaim to other cock-nightingales that he has staked out a territory and is prepared to defend it against all comers. And what makes him sing at night? A passion for the moon, a Baudelarian love of darkness? Not at all . . . it is because, like all the other members of his species, he has the kind of digestive system that makes him want to feed every four or five hours. . . . Between caterpillars . . . he warns his rivals. . . . When the eggs are hatched and territorial patriotism ceases to be necessary, a glandular change within the cock-nightingale's body puts a stop to all singing. Eternal pain and passion, the inviolable voice and the outpourings of ecstasy, give place to a silence, broken only by an occasional hoarse croak. [Therefore, the modern poet must harmonize the scientific truths about nightingales with] the truth about the human beings who listen to the nightingale's song, [for the new scientific facts] are a challenge from which it would be pusillanimous to shrink.[9]

It does not seem necessary for the poet or anyone else to shrink from these new scientific facts about the biology of the nightingale. It seems, rather, that they should be evaluated in their proper perspective and then quietly ignored as insignificant in the general scheme of things. Of course, it is well to have our misconceptions about nightingales corrected, but does it really matter in any significant way to know, for example, that it is the male, not the female, nightingale which sings? This fact seems quite unimportant in comparison with the knowledge that a healthy, vigorous nightingale, singing lustily at night, possesses what the Greeks called *arete*.

In Homeric times the word *arete* was an important part of the Greek vocabulary, signifying a particular quality in man or animal worthy of the highest admiration. With the passage of time many different kinds of *arete* were recognized and esteemed, yet in its most comprehensive sense the word denoted in the classical period that supreme excellence of which any living being is capable—that sum total of an individual's superior qualities. To be sure, such a concept of inherent excellence or "rightness" was a man-made concept of the Pre-Scientific World, but it is more than an intellectual abstraction. At the specific level, we know today that "rightness," in the sense of an harmonious adjustment to the environment, is a prerequisite for the existence of all species of plants and animals which now inhabit the earth; without it, they could not have survived the passage of evolutionary time. At the individual level—in those real objects which man perceives with his senses—the Greeks recognized, and delighted in, the relationship of a healthy, vigorous animal to its environment. They also knew that this inherent rightness or *arete* of an animal is concerned with fitness and therefore belongs rightly to itself. Furthermore, a nightingale in the full vigor of his nocturnal song not only embodies *arete* but also seems to experience, along with us who perceive him, some kind of *joie de vivre*. This contention cannot of course be proved, but I feel it must be true.

Lacking the objective knowledge of science, poets of the Pre-Scientific World could speak of nightingales only by recording the emotional response they evoked. Some poets of the Scientific Age followed this example by fearfully shutting their eyes to the scientific facts they knew about nightingales. I suppose others, with very little emotion at all, have preferred to regard the nightingale as a biological machine. Still others, including Aldous Huxley, wish to reconcile their emotional response to a nightingale with all the relevant scientific facts in the conviction that only in this way can knowledge of the wholeness of both men and nightingales be attained.

At a time when the two cultures are being so hotly debated, there remains still another possibility. For the Greeks recognized that the *arete* or supreme excellence of any living organism is concerned not only with fitness but also with purpose and the realization of its potential—and thereby they knew that it was an ultimate good. In doing so, they were thinking in terms of a wholeness of life which I believe transcends the sum total of all of the physical, chemical, taxonomic, morphological, physiological, ecological, and genetic facts which biologists have since accumulated. The Greek concept of *arete*, which seems to form such a natural basis for any poetry attempting to express wholeness both in the poet and in his living material, bears little relation to modern science. It partakes too directly of the spiritual world for that. It is a reflection of man's awareness of the good.

The *arete* of a nightingale embodies that which is good for nightingales; it is the basis of their survival. Therefore I do not share Huxley's opinion that it has been a major scientific triumph of recent years to recognize that for a nightingale, a nightingale is the measure of all things. Some Greeks knew this two millennia ago; Protagoras did not speak for them all. They also knew of the vast difference existing between avian *arete* and human *arete*. For a bird can strive no further than to live in complete harmony with its environment. This is to fulfill its "rightness" and to realize its highest potentiality. But for a man to live and propagate as a healthy, vigorous animal in blissful harmony with his environment represents only a fraction of human *arete*. The supreme excellence of which he is capable stretches further heavenward than that. Unique among all organisms in his awareness of the realm of the spirit, he strives to approach it, and only in the striving can he realize his potentialities and become as human as he is able.

I can think of no work of Greek literature that could serve as a suitable illustration of this specific difference between avian and human *arete*. On the other hand, a wonderfully appropriate example comes to mind from the literature of the twentieth century. It concerns a hawk.

The Hawk

In contrast to nightingales, hawks have not been loved by men. In the eighth century B.C. Hesiod set the tone by portraying in a fable a hawk as a cruel, proud, rapacious bird. Yet the essence of a hawk can be portrayed in quite another way. Twenty-seven centuries after Hesiod, a man of letters also spoke of hawks, in recounting what befell him as a young man, alone in the American wilderness. A naturalist by profession, he was there in the interest of science to collect live birds for the purpose of restocking a zoo. In a deserted mountain cabin he found two hawks and, with considerable difficulty, succeeded in capturing one of the pair. The next morning, he continues:

I was up early and brought the box in which the little hawk was imprisoned out onto the grass where I was building a cage. A wind as cool as a mountain spring ran over the grass and stirred my hair. It was a fine day to be alive. I looked up and all around and at the hole in the cabin roof out of which the other little hawk had fled. There was no sign of her anywhere that I could see.

"Probably in the next county by now," I thought cynically, but before beginning work I decided I'd have a look at my last night's capture.

Secretively, I looked again all around the camp and up and down and opened the box. I got him right out in my hand with his wings folded properly and I was careful not to startle him. He lay limp in my grasp and I could feel his heart pound under the feathers but he only looked beyond me and up.

I saw him look that last look away beyond me into a sky so full of light that I could not follow his gaze. The little breeze flowed over me again, and nearby a mountain aspen shook all its tiny leaves. I suppose I must have had an idea then of what I was going to do, but I never let it come up into consciousness. I just reached over and laid the hawk on the grass.

He lay there a long minute without hope, unmoving, his eyes still fixed on that blue vault above him. It must have been that he was already so far away in heart that he never felt the release from my hand. He never even stood. He just lay with his breast against the grass.

In the next second after that long minute he was gone. Like a flicker of light, he had vanished with my eyes full on him, but without actually seeing even a premonitory wing beat. He was gone straight into that towering emptiness of light and crystal that my eyes could scarcely bear to penetrate. For another long moment there was silence. I could not see him. The light was too intense. Then from far up somewhere a cry came ringing down.

I was young then and had seen little of the world, but when I heard that cry my heart turned over. It was not the cry of the hawk I had captured; for by shifting my position against the sun, I was now seeing further up. Straight out of the sun's eye, where she must have been soaring restlessly above us for untold hours, hurtled his mate. And from far up, ringing from peak to peak of the summits over us, came a cry of such unutterable and ecstatic joy that it sounds down across the years and tingles among the cups on my quiet breakfast table.

I saw them both now. He was rising fast to meet her. They met in a great soaring gyre that turned to a whirling circle and a dance of wings. Once more, just once, their two voices, joined in a harsh wild medley of question and response, struck and echoed against the pinnacles of the valley. Then they were gone forever somewhere into those upper regions beyond the eyes of men.[10]

It would be difficult to imagine a closer approach to the essence of avian *arete* than this recognition of the supreme excellence of which a bird is capable: to realize its highest potentiality by striving to live in harmony with its environment—and to derive joy therefrom. Yet, more important, these words reveal the essential difference between avian and human *arete*, for they also tell us of a man and his symbolic encounter with the realm of the spirit. Knowing that a captive hawk would be a source of interest, pleasure, and erudition to visitors at zoos, as well as to professional biologists, he is able to place this knowledge in its proper perspective—and in one fleeting moment the captive hawk is released, and the realm of the spirit is attained. And in the attainment, he becomes aware of what is good both for a bird and for a man.

Perhaps this symbolism represents the extreme manifestation of that spirituality which is the concern of the true poet: in this case, by *knowing* the excellence of his living material, he also *knows* the excellence for which he himself is striving. The result is not only submission to this knowledge but also active participation in it. Nor should it be forgotten that Eiseley's words, written only a few years ago, have already had widespread appeal. They seem to have gone straight into the hearts of men. What better evidence that the knowledge to which he submitted was some kind of superior knowledge?

From this one extreme of active participation in knowledge, there exist many other kinds of emotional responses of poets to their material. The passion, pain, and ecstasy evoked for untold ages by the nightingale, or, for that matter, any other form of life, have been accompanied by various degrees of participation, in which the poets approached the realm of the spirit and thereby the stuff of human greatness. If they succeeded in reaching this realm, their works partook of universality and endured. The point to be stressed here is that the poet's emotional awareness of spirituality—his love of excellence, of rightness, of *arete*, of the good —is in no way intensified by his acquisition of objective scientific knowledge. The fact that a bird's digestive and glandular systems are associated with its song is incontestable, but it is not superior knowledge nor is it a part of the spiritual world. It is simply of very little human significance. To believe otherwise is to maintain that the greatest and noblest works of art of the Pre-Scientific World were all lacking in some essential human quality, which contemporary and future poets, having the facts of science at their disposal, will be able to supply. In the second half of the twentieth century this view is not only invalid: it is also dangerous.

The literary art embodied in Eiseley's words about the hawk demonstrates what a contemporary poet can do by ignoring scientific knowledge. That he happens to be a professional scientist as well only strengthens the conviction that there is some radical defect in the basic assumption underlying the current debate on the two cultures. This assumption is that from the standpoint of evolutionary progress, man's increasing wholeness is dependent upon his increasing attainment of new knowledge. Let us now consider the concepts of knowledge and wholeness in their relation to the two cultures.

Another View of the Two Cultures

A particularly relevant statement by Aldous Huxley will serve admirably as an introduction to this part of the discussion: "The pre-condition of any fruitful relationship between literature and science is knowledge."[11] He then referred to the desirability of a two-way flow of knowledge between poets and scientists. But what I think he really meant to emphasize by this statement was a one-way flow, for in the passage that followed he laid most weight upon the new knowledge science is acquiring, which, he believed, should lead both scientists and poets to a deeper understanding of reality. Every new truth, every new fact, every new thought is thus to be welcomed as an addition to man's wholeness and as an aid in bridging the two cultures.

This universally accepted *Weltbild* reflects so much irresponsible optimism that it necessitates the very relevant question, "What kind of knowledge are we seeking, and why?" At present there is only one answer: In the name of human progress we are seeking, with very little discrimination, all possible kinds of new knowledge. Only by all of the knowable unknown becoming known, can man become whole.

Wholeness implies that nothing is lacking. Therefore the concept of wholeness, as applied to man, cannot be dissociated from human evolution, for everyone agrees that *Homo sapiens* is still a most imperfect species standing in need of drastic improvement. And everyone hopes that man's deficiencies will gradually be put right during the course of his future evolution. Thus, to attain human wholeness, either on the specific or the individual level, is to become supplied with that which one lacks—certainly a supremely desirable attainment. Yet the overwhelming and multitudinous totality of human imperfection makes it difficult to be subjectively certain about which deficiencies most need to be remedied. Notwithstanding, men of our day, with unwavering assurance, are collectively agreed that their lack of new knowledge is their supreme lack, which must therefore be supplied at all costs and as rapidly as possible.

This point of view stems naturally from the scientific world outlook, which, laying most weight upon quantitative expansion, is in itself essentially indiscriminate. Science, experimental or descriptive, is concerned with the perception and explanation of *all* parts of the universe and therefore necessarily involves the acquisition of many unessential new facts. Furthermore, such facts then often form the basis of new scientific visions and perspectives. To illustrate: scientists, whose prime concern is with objective description, measurement, and experimentation, are now investigating man in the same way; this approach has resulted, among other things, in a recent proposal to erect a biology of philosophy based upon the measurement of the electrical oscillations of the human brain. Since science prides itself upon its objectivity and its divorce from emotion and ethics, it cannot be otherwise.

Man's uniqueness among living organisms rests upon his awareness of the realm of the spirit, and this science denies. Even if, as Polanyi maintains,[12] modern scientists are far less objective than they themselves believe, their present activities *per se* cannot enhance man's essential humanness. Nevertheless, their unrestricted and indiscriminate attacks upon every unknown aspect of the organic and inorganic worlds are considered by the society in which they live to be of supreme importance. We witness today a tremendous increase in the number of institutions of learning that specialize in scientific and technological knowledge, but we rarely even contemplate the founding of an institution of learning devoted to morals and ethics. Intelligence is evaluated so much higher than virtue that we overemphasize to the point of idolatry the attainment and dissemination of new objective knowledge. To question in any way these means for the indiscriminate and quantitative expansion of our "noosphere" is considered one of the most flagrant heresies of the twentieth century. Fortunately, there will always be heretics.

Farrington, in characterizing much of modern science as "mindless and heartless," writes: "It worries me to think of all the new universities rising from English soil, with less and less evidence that they are thinking about what they are doing."[13] He also points out the seldom mentioned fact that even Francis Bacon was so aware of the potential risks of advances in knowledge that he expressed the desire that "knowledge is to be limited by religion."

Equally relevant are the heretical views of a man of letters who, in the 1920s, as we have seen, welcomed the poet's use of all new scientific knowledge and its application. Mumford's recent address on the automation of knowledge is a long diatribe against the whole blind system of compulsive advance in knowledge of our day, be it in science or scholarship.[14] With foresight and astuteness he has succeeded in exposing the dangers of this system not only to man but to the system itself: for he reasons quite rightly that it may, in the end, collapse by its own senseless overproductivity. To suppose that man's wholeness can be substantially enhanced by a system based upon the irresponsible, indiscriminate, and quantitative automation of knowledge is wishful thinking. Basically, such a system is unplanned, heartless, and—despite all the logic and rationalism of the scientific outlook —mindless as well: for, as Mumford points out, it has already become an absurd end in itself which is most probably doomed to self-destruction.

The enormous error inherent in our compulsive desire to attain new knowledge is that we forget that human progress demands that our primary concern be only with that knowledge which is humanly significant. To attain it depends entirely upon our ability to discriminate between the qualitative and the quantitative aspects of man's wholeness. If we are able to do this, we must at the same time recognize that one of the greatest perils of our times is the continued, all-out expansion of our "noosphere." For however orderly all the newly acquired facts appear to be arranging themselves, the expansion itself is a wholly indiscriminate human attainment; its explosive and unassimilated nature alone should arouse serious doubts as to whether it is leading to a satisfactory *Weltbild* based upon man's enhanced wholeness and understanding of reality. Already this waxing "noosphere" is becoming uncontrollable and is increasing, in countless ways, the chaotic complexity of life, whose essential aspects are thereby becoming increasingly obscured. To this prospect must be added a continually mounting fear of the dehumanizing use to which all this new knowledge may be put. The recent past has already given us a foretaste of the horrors of applied science, but this may prove to be only child's play.

No one can question Aldous Huxley's acute awareness of the awful prospects of the application of science—the nuclear weapons, the chemical and radioactive pollution of the earth (including, incidentally, the eradication of nightingales), the creation of a race of supermen by well-meaning eugenists. Yet when he earnestly desired that poets should join hands with scientists to advance "further and further into the ever expanding regions of the unknown," he seemed to be unaware that his desire might be impossible of fulfillment. I do not mean because of the unforeseeable, accidentally disastrous consequences of scientific research, but because the human progress that is sought by many eminent biologists involves their controlling and directing human thought through genetic, chemical, and perhaps even surgical interference. It follows that the mental capacities of the poets who are to advance into the unknown may be so radically transformed that they would be incapable of any longer thinking and acting like poets. And to judge from the contributions to our Scientific Age by the literary avant-garde, it seems that many of them are already incapable of doing so.

Another point to consider is Aldous Huxley's contention that because science has "explained" changes in human emotion as physico-chemical alterations in our bodies, poets can no longer attribute such happenings to supernatural intervention. "For the twentieth-century man of letters," he writes, "this temptingly easy way out is barred. The only explanatory hypotheses that it is permissible to incorporate into a contemporary poem about changing moods are those of contemporary science."[15] This mechanistic approach to human emotion is to deny the uniqueness of human *arete* by refusing to admit that of all living beings, man is most deeply aware of the realm of the spirit. Scientific research on both man and animals has yielded many findings about the chemical and physical state of the body during those periods of ineffable happiness or grief that most healthy individuals experience. Yet however much knowledge has been acquired, and however much the transient peaks and depressions of human moods can be artificially simulated or transformed, no scientist alive today can disprove the view that the endocrinology of elation and despair is a secondary effect of the activity of the human soul, which, in itself, remains primary.

The chief significance of scientific knowledge about human emotions lies in the fact that those who possess it are able, if they wish, to apply it to the mental and spiritual transformation of mankind. They believe that thereby mankind will be improved. Yet can anything be more inherently absurd than the desire to make men more god-like through drugs and surgery? One need only reflect that the methods scientists would employ to attain this higher state of humanness would be necessarily derived from that kind of knowledge which is furthest from the spiritual realm. The result of their efforts could only be an artificial, degraded spirituality and a general retreat of the human spirit.

Despite the perils of the dehumanizing applications of science, the belief persists in the current debate on the two cultures that a rapidly expanding "noosphere" is both inevitable and desirable and that a bridge must be built between the world of science and that of literature. To recapitulate, the two basic reasons for this belief are:

(1) That of Snow: We must help the needy to attain the primal things, and this we can best do through increasing knowledge and increasing cooperation between scientists and poets.

(2) That of Huxley: We must advance into the unknown, scientists and poets together, so that the new knowledge attained will lead to a deeper understanding of reality and thereby make all of us more whole.

Snow's proposal has been called a "brave new vision," and in a sense this is true. For it is a fervent, philanthropic appeal, calling for still further effort upon the part of scientists and technologists to alleviate human suffering. Moreover, to counterbalance and humanize scientific progress, he suggests that a greater emphasis be placed upon the literary education of future scientists. Huxley's eloquent and thought-provoking vision likewise reflects a sincere desire to make the best of both the scientific and the spiritual aspects of the universe by uniting them for the benefit of all mankind.

Of course we must alleviate human suffering, but, as Snow himself points out, we already know how to do it. In other words, the objective knowledge necessary for this purpose is ours: it need only be disseminated. But this is no justification for continuing to increase this knowledge at the same mad rate as at present, or for continuing to make it an end in itself and thereby valuing intelligence above virtue. Granted, these trends will lead to an improvement in living standards, but even with Snow's humanizing correctives, they would not enhance human wholeness. Nor would Huxley's vision of the scientific conquest of the unknown enhance it any more. For both proposals call for an amalgamation of all of the knowledge from the world of science and the world of literature in order to create an ever-expanding "noosphere" of indiscriminate quantitative wholeness.

Another proposal remains. It in no way dismisses either Snow's altruism or Huxley's desire for wholeness. It is concerned with quality rather than quantity and is therefore directed away from the concept of the "noosphere." This proposal is that both poets and scientists should discriminate between the humanly superfluous and the humanly significant and, by ignoring the former, create a transcending world of qualitative wholeness. This proposal would necessitate a moral renewal both in literature and science and the retardation of what is now called progress.

Is this a reactionary, obscurantist, cowardly vision, made out of the idealist's purported desire for permanency and his fear of growth and change? Let those who wish, call it so. Others may see in it a demand for greater courage and development than that embodied in the concept of the expanding "noosphere." For scientists, borrowing from the world of letters the idea of moral progress, would be able to view their own activity in its proper perspective and therefore continue it in a more humanly desirable manner and tempo. And poets would also advance more slowly; prizing science for supplying to mankind its material needs and its objective knowledge about the universe, they would nevertheless use as their prime source of material that most difficultly accessible superior knowledge which only the greatest of their predecessors were able to attain. Without this awareness, on both sides, of what the Greeks called sophrosyne and without its concomitant moral restraint, the continued progress of the scientific and the literary avant-gardes will most probably lead man into a permanent state of absurdity and amorality by the irrevocable transformation of his genes, his mind, and his spirit.

Yet the hope exists that man, for all his imperfections, is now sufficiently evolved to be able to choose, before it is too late, that knowledge he most lacks: that which can make him qualitatively whole. On the basis of what has already been said about nightingales and hawks, the choice advocated here should now be obvious: most worthy of attainment is that knowledge of *arete*, of the good, and of human greatness—that knowledge which most closely approaches the realm of the spirit. I believe this to be superior knowledge of the most significant kind, and, further, that the lack of it is responsible for man's not being whole. The problems each human being has to confront arise out of the contrasting essentials of life—happiness and grief, love and hate, success and failure, health and disease, gratification and frustration—and the manner in which he responds to them is a measure of his wholeness. If he has knowledge of spiritual values, he responds in a way that assures his gradual growth into a more human individual, and with it the progressive evolution of the species to which he belongs.

But to believe that the ability to embrace and assimilate life can be substantially enhanced by the indiscriminate acquisition of more and more objective knowledge denotes a failure to recognize that modern science, as we know it today, is too far divorced from human values to elevate human wholeness. We forget that discriminative choice is also a human activity, which, when applied to knowledge, could insure human progress. *Homo sapiens* has always needed to expand his knowledge, but at this stage of his history, his pressing need is for the qualitative expansion of the humanly significant portion.

This portion is that superior knowledge, which, being closest of all knowledge to the realm of the spirit, is chiefly concerned with moral values: *arete*, the good, the excellent, the right. In this vision human *arete* is no classical Greek concept to be condescendingly admired at leisure and then to be hastily discarded in confrontation with twentieth-century reality. It is a heart-warming, enduring goal, giving purpose, meaning, and strength to the individual's struggle to realize his highest potential. What more humanly desirable attainment for poets and scientists alike?

VI

Humanism and the Rhesus

We must not do as some recommend and, being men, think but human thoughts, or, being mortals, think but mortal thoughts; but, as far as possible, we should play the immortal and strive to live according to the highest that is in us.＊
—*Aristotle*, Nicomachean Ethics, *1177b.*

Humanism, Historical and Modern

The word humanism, as everyone knows, was originally associated with the Renaissance, having first been applied to that rising surge of concern for human excellence which had been set in motion by the medieval scholars' discovery of their heritage. But as Morris Bishop has so aptly remarked, it is a "seductive word, distorted to fit numberless modern uses."[1] To have validity, a twentieth-century discussion of humanism ought therefore to be introduced by a definition and delimitation of the concept in both its historical and its contemporary context.

This is by no means an easy task. Even though the essence of all humanism is the human potential, modern standards and appraisals of human excellence are extraordinarily diversified and

＊ Basil Wrighton's translation.

often in vehement opposition. Still, anyone today who speaks about humanism not only desires to appear as a true humanist working to improve the human lot but also prides himself, tacitly or openly, on being one. In this dehumanizing age of war, violence, and explosive scientific and technological advance, the word humanism rings comfortingly in many ears, however unequal their ability to hear its fundamental tone. But the humanists of our day, just as many in the past, have mistaken the overtones for the fundamental. The semantic changes that have gradually befallen the word humanism all seem to be changes for the worse and tend to obscure its original meaning. Humanism, as a twentieth-century concept, may need a thoroughgoing reevaluation if it is ever to become a unifying and enduring goal for our descendants.

The term "historical humanism" can be restricted to the upsurge of human vitality during the Renaissance or it can be extended still further backward to include the driving force behind the creativity of the ancient world. To grasp the fundamental tone of humanism requires going back to classical times—but not because of Protagoras' dictum that man is the measure of all things, and not because of Terence's discovery that because he was a man, all things human were his concern. The fundamental tone is not made of such stuff. Rather, it is necessarily composed of two indissolubly related ingredients: (1) a concern for the past and (2) a concern for religion. I do not believe it can be otherwise: the supreme excellence of which man is capable—that which the Greeks called human *arete*—can be attained only through a knowledge of man's past greatness in confrontation with his gods. An enduring standard of human greatness is indispensable for genuine humanists; they must necessarily lead lives in which, to use Benjamin Farrington's fine phrase, they "think with the whole of their past" about sacred as well as secular things.[2]

The fundamental tone of humanism, as understood here, is thus man's preoccupation with the record of the limits of the human potential in order to become more god-like and surpass himself. Such humanism, in contrast to past and present distortions, is further regarded as the primary basis of human progress, both on the individual and on the specific level. To illustrate, let us stop a moment before the memory of Plato. His critical concern with the Homeric legacy in education, his loathing of the widespread immorality of his own time and his longing for an earlier Golden Age, his interest in the mysticism and spiritual aspirations of the Orphics who preceded him, his eugenic proposals to improve the human race, his unceasing preoccupation with *arete* and the divine in his striving to nourish the human soul, and, finally, his courageous attempts to live his words in Sicily—all these things combine to form the embodiment of humanism as it is envisaged here.

Sixteen hundred years later a new embodiment appeared in the person of Petrarch. Justly deserving the title of the founder of Renaissance humanism, he opened the eyes of the fourteenth century to its heritage through his admiration and reverence for the humanists of the classical world and through his hope that a loving and emulative knowledge of past greatness would be posterity's most precious possession. At the same time, let it be remembered, he was a devout Catholic who so adored Saint Augustine that it was to him, and to no other, that he turned in his moment of spiritual exaltation at the summit of Mont Ventoux. His concern with past greatness was primarily limited to a firsthand knowledge of the Latin heritage. "I have read," he tells us, "Virgil, Horace, Livy, and Cicero not once but a thousand times, not hastily but dwelling on them. They are not only in my mind but in my marrow; they are a part of myself."* Yet had he been able to read Plato's original words, his devotion to past knowledge would have been immeasurably enhanced. What

* Morris Bishop's translation.

inspiration he might have derived from reading, for example, in the *Phaedrus*, Socrates' prayer to Eros:

δίδου τ'ἔτι μᾶλλον ἢ νῦν παρὰ τοῖς καλοῖς τίμιον εἶναι.
(Grant to me even more than now to be esteemed among the fair.)

Petrarch's ignorance of the Greek language, which he himself so deplored, was as much our loss as his.

Following Petrarch, the leading humanist scholars of the Renaissance were, like him, deeply religious men, preoccupied with the *mysterium tremendum* of the relation between the human and the divine and therefore immersed in all that their heritage had to tell them. Hearing humanism's fundamental tone, they could, of course, do no other.

Yet it was the overtones that most Renaissance humanists heard. These overtones, stressing the developmental, transitory, and inconstant aspects of human existence, are based upon an indiscriminate interest in human affairs rather than upon a definitive and meaningful idea. For they proclaim that human life directs itself, and so long as it moves, all is well; our glorious intellectual capacities, unchecked, unquestioned, and unguided, will somehow ensure the realization of the human potential.

The unrestrained delight which the men of the early Renaissance had in their own prospective worth was derived from their discovery of the human *arete* of the classical world. But most of them failed to recognize that the noblest forms of *arete*, arising out of the human-divine interrelation, are the enduring basis of moral guidance. Hearing mostly the overtones, they began to look upon all forms of ecclesiastical orthodoxy and authority as mere hindrances to their life work. Others, with equal pride in their own native ability, began such a thorough exploration of their earthly environment that their present-day descendants, having mastered most of it, are now renouncing all forms of traditional spiritual knowledge in favor of new scientific knowledge. Like twentieth-century humanists, Renaissance humanists, with few exceptions, cared not to emulate or participate. Thus, in their time "the educated classes in Italy lost their grip upon morality . . . the Christian virtues were scorned . . . while the antique virtues were themes for rhetoric rather than moving springs of conduct."[3] So it is when man believes himself wiser than his gods.

The humanists of our Scientific Age not only hear the overtones —they are deafened by them. To the great majority of modern humanists a preoccupation with the human-divine relationships of the past would be incomprehensible. Humanism, for them, means a concern for the human potential in the present and the future, and nowhere else. The record of human greatness, they say, can have only passing interest for the twentieth century, since all the greatness of the Pre-Scientific World was attained through a false belief in the divine. And the skies *are* empty. Has not Nietzsche's contention that God is dead been substantiated by science and confirmed by the projections of modern psychology? We, who know better than our predecessors, have rid ourselves of their puerile belief in the supernatural and are therefore destined to make greater headway than they. In order to "jettison the once noble but now mouldering myths",[4] twentieth-century man—emancipated, enlightened, and rational—has at last come of age.

One need not be a classical scholar or a Christian to feel a deep and abiding resentment at this pseudo-humanism. One is overwhelmed by the monstrous arrogance of it all, just as Goethe was overwhelmed on hearing of some scornful attempt to dispose of Euripides' greatness by a man of far lesser stature. One so well understands a contemporary classical scholar whose recent book on the origin, development, and survival of humanism passes over all forms of modern humanism in complete silence.[5] And one wholeheartedly concurs in a recent critical characterization of the prevalent attitude of our times: "What modern man can or cannot believe is the test of truth."[6]

Furthermore, for those who with mind and heart together believe that a humanist, to be worthy of the name, must base his life and works upon the record of the human-divine interrelationship, the commitment of twentieth-century humanists to demolish religion, idealism, absolute values, and traditional morality appears extraordinarily negative. For all they have to offer instead is a faith in the never-ending accumulation of new scientific knowledge about man and the universe in order to increase human understanding. Ronald Hepburn has said that modern humanists seem to lack an object of reverence and awe,[7] yet their interest in the unceasing advance of science appears so idolatrous that I would think they must regard scientific investigation as some kind of sacred human endeavor. Man has no immortal soul, they tell us, yet he is unique because, in contrast to lower animals, he can reason and thus has the intellectual ability to choose that which is best for him. And what do they consider "best"? That scientific knowledge which ensures his health, happiness, and survival. Since they are aware that the species may be doomed to ultimate extinction on earth by cosmic forces beyond its control, and since they believe that death is final, then survival in the sense of not dying before one's time becomes of transcendent importance. So important, in fact, that survival both on the individual and the specific level apparently becomes another sacred notion for modern humanists—such a common-sense attitude, they say, must rationally surpass all others. And then, without a shred of supporting evidence, they dogmatically proclaim that there are no other worlds for us than the one we know. *Ergo,* only temporal human existence, with the accent on the present moment, has meaning.

The most inspired and enlightened teachers of any age have taught those who would listen that it is not preoccupation with survival and earthly bliss but striving after knowledge of the Good—and participation in it—which determines whether the human potential is to be realized. Modern humanists are not unaware of this fact: they admit it is "awkward" for them to accept that great deeds have been done by those who, with no thought of happiness or survival, knew what they *ought* to do. They even condescend to say that "the answers [to the question, "What is the Good Life?"] given by the great thinkers of the past cannot be brushed aside as wholly irrelevant to our needs."[8] Yet in spite of their inability to understand a morality based upon a passionate love of ideals and absolutes, *arete* and divinity, they stoutly maintain that "those who reject the humanist rejection of the absolute know not what they do. They want their flowers in wax or in flame, but these are not flowers."[9] So they continue to challenge those in a Scientific Age who still believe in traditional morality and in the existence of divinity, even though they consider them helpless, blind, and deluded victims of emotional starvation with whom it is impossible to argue rationally. They can, they say, "only marvel and pass on."[10]

All right. Let us accept the challenge and play their own game. Let us call them back to demonstrate—rationally—that it is they themselves who have not yet heard humanism's fundamental tone.

The Rhesus Monkey in the Modern World Picture

The rhesus or macaque, is an East Indian monkey (*Macaca mulata*) that has of late been bred in captivity to supply experimental psychologists with objects for their investigations. Since the emotional responses of the young of this species appear similar to those of the human infant, some long-term experiments designed by H. F. Harlow and his associates at the University of Wisconsin were carried out to throw light upon the nature of love in man as well as monkeys. Scientists appear to disagree whether the initial love response of the human being to its mother is innate or a secondary effect of such primary drives as hunger or thirst; accordingly, the infant-mother emotional response in these monkeys was analyzed. As the studies progressed, they were extended to include the infant-infant affectional system, as well as the developmental behavior of some of the test animals during the course of several years of observation. In 1958, in a presidential address to a meeting of the American Psychological Association, Professor Harlow told his audience:

Love is a wondrous state, deep, tender, and rewarding. Because of its intimate and personal nature it is regarded by some as an improper topic for experimental research. But, whatever our personal feelings may be, our assigned mission as psychologists is to analyze all facets of human and animal behavior into their component variables. So far as love or affection is concerned, psychologists have failed in this mission.[11]

So much for the scientific justification of the experiments. That the first results had been highly successful appears in the words with which Harlow concluded his address: ". . . it is comforting to know that we are now in contact with the nature of love."

The results were obtained by comparing "normal" behavior with the abnormal behavior of animals subjected to partial or complete isolation and/or provided with surrogate mothers. As to general methodology, we are told that "we know that we are better monkey mothers than are real monkey mothers thanks to synthetic diets, vitamins, iron extracts, penicillin, chloromycetin, 5 percent glucose, and constant, tender, loving care." The last four words, however, might well be italicized, for we are next told that "a baby monkey raised on a bare wire-mesh cage floor survives with difficulty, if at all, during the first five days of life."

The surrogate mothers were constructed of wire and covered with cloth and were designed "to produce a perfectly proportioned, streamlined body stripped of unnecessary bulges and appendices." This mother had a head, two eyes, and one breast, and she radiated heat from a light bulb placed behind her. The infant monkeys were found to "love" the physical contact she provided—in fact, even when she provided no nourishment, they preferred her warmth and softness to a surrogate mother supplying milk but made of wire alone. In experiments in which the baby monkeys were placed in a strange place without their surrogate mothers, they were found to "rush across the test room and throw themselves face down on the floor, clutching their heads and bodies and screaming their distress." Baby monkeys who had known only wire mothers from birth "would run to some wall or corner of the room, clasp their heads and bodies and rock convulsively back and forth." These experiments showed, we are told, that the love responses of monkeys were not based upon the reduction of hunger or thirst, and that the "deep and abiding bond between mother and child appears to be essentially the same, whether the mother is real or a cloth surrogate."[12]

In other isolation experiments fifty-six baby monkeys taken from their mothers a few hours after birth were kept alone from five to eight years in bare wire cages where they could see and hear other monkeys but had no physical contact with them. Their abnormal behavior is described thus:

> The laboratory-born monkeys sit in their cages and stare fixedly into space, circle their cages in a repetitive stereotyped manner and clasp their heads in their hands or arms and rock for long periods of time. They often develop compulsive habits—the animal may chew and tear at its body until it bleeds.[13]

They were also sexually abnormal, and we are told that "the entire group of animals separated from their mothers at birth and raised in individual wire cages, with or without surrogate, must be written off as potential breeding stock."

The most unfortunate monkeys of all, however, were those that were subjected to total isolation. Following birth, each was housed alone in a cubicle with solid walls, its behavior being observed by one-way vision screens and tested by remote control. Their solitary confinement lasted for two years, *during which time they saw no living creature except themselves.* Upon removal from their cubicles (and what an interesting day that must have been for the psychologists!), their emotional disturbance was so great that even after another two-year period in which they were all kept together in one cage, they still exhibited abnormal fear of other living creatures.

Since these experiments on total isolation were reported in 1962, it appears that the views Harlow had expressed in 1959 concerning the ultimate aim of his work were still considered valid. At that time he wrote:

> The first love of the human infant is for his mother. The tender intimacy of this attachment is such that it is sometimes regarded as a sacred or mystical force, an instinct incapable of analysis . . . such compunctions . . . have hampered experimental observations of the bonds between child and mother. . . . The further exploitation of the broad field of research that now opens up depends merely upon the availability of infant monkeys . . . there is no reason why we cannot at some future time investigate the fundamental neurophysiological and biochemical variables underlying affection and love.[14]

Harlow has been criticized recently for transferring concepts from the field of human psychology to the field of animal behavior because in his experiments the "love or affection" of the infant monkeys for the surrogate mothers could be better explained as imprinting.[15] I believe that criticism of the rhesus experiments should rest on a deeper foundation than ethology: to conduct a scientific investigation of the emotional responses of acutely distressed laboratory animals and call it a "contact with the nature of love" reveals a profound unawareness of the limitations of science. And what is more important in the present context, it provides at the same time an admirable illustration of the basic outlook of modern secular and scientific humanism.

Modern Humanism's Response to the Rhesus Experiments

Modern humanism must enthusiastically approve the rhesus experiments and, in fact, it does. I refer to a specific response to these experiments from one of the leading scientific humanists of our day, who describes them as "fascinating studies."[16] Not a doubt of their human validity, not a mention of the ethical aspects involved, not a condemnatory word about the permanently abnormal states of the test objects, but only wholehearted approval ending with the statement that "it will be extremely interesting" to see further results. Obviously, when one regards a rational morality as the sole standard of human conduct, then one must assent to the aims and methods of experimental psychologists who wish to analyze all aspects of human behavior.

In our Scientific Age it is generally believed that man has no divine spark or immortal soul and differs from animals only by his more highly developed brain and nervous system and his high degree of consciousness. *Ergo,* the study of the emotional behavior of subhuman primates is naturally believed to provide knowledge that will increase man's understanding of himself. Contemporary psychologists who deny that the infant-mother relation on the animal level can be spoken of in terms of devotion or affection have nevertheless considered such emotional responses to represent the primitive beginnings of the human condition.[17]

Contemporary humanists, in their renunciation of divinity and whatever else might lie beyond the realm of natural phenomena, desire that human love be scientifically proven to be the ultimate expression of animal emotion, grounded in the Nature we are able to perceive. From the evolutionary point of view, human love is looked upon as the ultimate expression of anthropoid emotion and has thus no more claim than it to be sacrosanct. Science is encouraged to investigate, observationally and experimentally, all the diverse manifestations of human and subhuman emotions by any means at its disposal. Nothing that *is* can lie beyond the reach of the rationality of objective science. Psychology's present strivings to extend its frontiers through experiments designed to shed light upon normal and abnormal human behavior can, the humanists tell us, be of immense benefit to mankind: we must therefore heed carefully its pronouncements on the nature of love.

To condemn the rhesus experiments for what they are—odious

examples of cruelty to animals that degrade the humanness of those who designed and perpetrated them—obviously does not appeal to modern humanists. Besides opposing their aims, condemnation would constitute a barrier to free inquiry and the attainment of truth. Humanists are, of course, no more insensitive to animal suffering than anyone else and probably much more sensitive than most. They are also awake to the dangers of the misuse of applied science and technology. *But they cannot rationally object to an experimental science that depends upon animal suffering for its results when they believe that such results will augment human health, happiness, and survival.* For these ends, they maintain, are our supreme ends. Secular and scientific humanists, it must be remembered, have no standard of morality whatsoever except the rational.

Yet the rhesus experiments on "the nature of love" lead far beyond the ethics of animal experimentation. Since any attempt to convince, persuade, or even intimate that human love is associated with the supernatural is hastily rejected by modern humanists, it is understandable that they have disparaged the efforts of the Bishop of Woolwich to make the secular sacred.[18] For although his end is similar to theirs, his means are essentially different. Humanists attempt to show that the secular is "sacred" because human reason reveals that there is nothing more. Dr. Robinson attempts to show that although the traditional tenets of Christianity appear to be doomed in a Scientific Age, the love that the Christian religion gave to mankind through Jesus Christ might one day so pervade every aspect of daily living that the secular must inevitably become sacred. This twentieth-century theological interpretation of Christianity and the recent publicity it has received from the hands of Dr. Robinson dismays the humanists, who cannot accept any form of spiritual revelation as the basis of secular living.

As a consequence, they attempt either to demonstrate the bishop's grave error in stating that God is ultimate reality (since the twentieth century *knows* that He is merely a man-made hypothesis),[19] or to maintain that the success of the book is not due to any intellectual worth but to emotional pronouncements about love by a man who is desperately clinging to a useless and outmoded religion,[20] or to express hopeful doubts that his views will make Christianity more acceptable, since Christian love, being based upon narrowly concentrated individual relations, has already proved to be an unworkable ethic.[21] What these objections to secular Christianity amount to, of course, is that modern humanists fear that others might steal their fire. *Their* rational message must not be replaced by an emotional message: the hope of a better world lies with humanism's reason, not with idealism's love. Evolution has shown that love is nothing more than a biological necessity for man and animal alike, and they believe that this should be sufficient for our enlightened Scientific Age.

Being thus uneasy before the potential power of a love over which they could exercise no control, and being guided by the claims of a rational morality, modern humanists can have no reasonable justification for protesting against Harlow's experiments. On the contrary, they wish psychology to delve even deeper into the nature of anthropoid love. Since we are unique, they say, because we are super-rational animals, it is reason, not emotion, that will permit us to realize our potential. Therefore, love, being a biological necessity, cannot have its origins in another world; it is of the earth, and nothing more. It must be investigated by the rational objectivity of science.

I believe, with modern humanists, that the essence of humanism is the realization of the human potential. But I do not believe it can ever be realized by the means they prescribe—for they hear only the overtones of humanism.

The Rhesus Experiments and Humanism's Fundamental Tone

Of course, it is undeniable that the great development of our brain and nervous system has permitted us to attain objective knowledge about the universe by which we can master our environment, ensure our survival, and control our future. Without this preliminary step, human evolution could not have entered into its present psychosocial stage. We are conscious and we know it. We think, reason, symbolize, abstract, and communicate in ways that enormously exceed the mental capacities of animals. But we are also separated from them by much more than this. I speak now of our awareness of a spiritual realm and its bearing upon our concepts of morality, values, and ethics—this human faculty which the Scientific Age so confidently regards as the ultimate by-product of animal neurophysiology.[22]

Actually, it has no rational grounds for doing so. It has no positive evidence for concluding that the scientific world picture represents the sole source of truth. It has no basis for maintaining that the supernatural is really "transnatural" because it has grown out of ordinary nature.[23] It cannot disprove that the heroes, saints, and philosophers were divinely inspired when they looked up to heaven to find the meaning of human existence. If the scientific *Weltbild* were correct—if morality had grown out of biological necessity, and if science were able to trace back every aspect of man's emotional and intellectual make-up to subhuman beginnings—then the last few millennia should have witnessed a tremendous progressive development of ethics and morals in keeping with our new time scale arising out of the explosive development of psychosocial evolution. In this sordid century of outrageous wars, violence, and criminality, no one can contend that this has happened. On the contrary, these are all grounds for believing that Hebrew, Buddhistic, Socratic, and Christian teachings were on an infinitely higher ethical level than the dicta of a humanism that foresees the subversion of teleological attitudes and which teaches that the Good Life means to increase secular bliss and ensure its survival.

In other words, a highly developed concept of morality was already existent in the early stages of psychosocial evolution but has not yet shown any signs of explosive evolutionary development. Even though this morality was intensified by the cumulative efforts of the most enlightened individuals of all ages, it has gradually lost its vitality. It has been merely passively transmitted along with all the rest of our cultural heritage as our traditional morality—that which now appears so quaint and impotent to a Scientific Age. Yet, however vehemently the twentieth century may deny it, it is this traditional morality that has played a decisive role in giving each one of us a spiritual concept of the Good, an awareness of the existence of another realm transcending our own, and, in varying degrees, a subjective certainty that love is at the base of it all.

If contemporary scientists and humanists wish to talk reasonably about love in evolution, they commit a grave error in disregarding the psychosocial record. All manifestations of human *arete* of which we have record partook of love in some form. Above all, they should pay heed to the *Symposium*, in which one of the most illumined minds of all time recorded his thoughts about its ultimate nature. Plato knew that love is love of something which one lacks, and since what each one of us most lacks is more knowledge of the Good, it seems well to conclude, with him, that the ultimate nature of human love must be concerned with love of this knowledge.

And since the essence of humanism is man's ability to realize his potential—or surpass it, if possible—then his love of knowledge of the Good and his striving to incorporate it into himself become his means for doing so. Contrary to what modern humanists believe, this Good to which man is committed is more than what is good for his earthly survival. The accent is rather on knowledge of the divine aspect of the human-divine interrelation —that which is permanent, unchanging, absolute. The most enlightened humanists of any age have been aware of this: they sought enduring knowledge, for they knew that no human potential could ever be realized without it.

Now, in the twentieth century, humanists are glorifying the human species because it has become so infinitely wise that it has no gods at all. There is no longer any ultimate purpose in life, no traditional moral code, no enduring *arete* to emulate—only evolutionary change and developmental flux. Science has discovered that the human potential can be realized by life directing itself, provided that scientists be permitted to investigate every aspect of its existence. Love belongs to life and has its origins in the primal protoplasmic ooze. Let the psychologists be supplied with all the animals they need to investigate its nature. We must put human behavior on a scientific foundation. And who can stop us? We are alone in the universe.

If human love be only of this world, then scientists and humanists are certainly right: nothing can stop them from further investigating human emotion and behavior and thereby directing the course of evolution by their rational morality. As one humanist has so confidently put it, the behavioral sciences "have reached a point at which, for the first time in history, the Humanist can reasonably attempt an integrated naturalistic approach to love."[24] *But if human love is more than human,* the perspectives are at once changed. A love whose origins are not of this world is the only force I can think of that would be capable of causing scientists and humanists to exercise self-restraint—provided, of course, their consciousness permitted them to recognize its supernatural nature. For only a divine love can reveal to man the scientific world picture for what it is—a woefully inadequate picture of "reality."

Harlow's experiments have shown that emotional satisfaction is necessary for the well-being and survival of monkeys who have neither knowledge nor love of the Good. What, therefore, have his experiments to do with the essential nature of love? Does Harlow not know that human love embraces kindness, mercy, and compassion, as well as respect for all life? Can he seriously maintain that experiments involving the deliberate infliction of intense and prolonged mental suffering on animals can yield results applicable to human love, when they so debase it? Does he not know that human love differs qualitatively from animal love? Does he not know that a human mother is unique because she has an abstract idea of the Good and that therefore human love, unlike animal love, has its ontogenetic beginnings in a spiritual bond between mother and child? And, finally, does he not know that the surest way to understand love, be it maternal, paternal, filial, agapeic, erotic, or Platonic, is to experience whatever forms one can?

Recent thoughts about the evolution of consciousness may be of much relevance to this discussion.[25] Contrary to the expectations of modern psychologists, the further development of man's consciousness may lead the human species right out of the Scientific Age. All of us may gradually become aware that human love partakes of the divine and that it has its origins in the spiritual realm beyond our perceptible realm of natural phenomena. A reaction against the diametrically opposed *Weltbild* of science is conceivable in the not too distant future. Already there are indications of a growing awareness that there is more to human life than all the extensions of modern biology will ever be able to penetrate.

I believe this "more" to be that which *transcends* life—the permanent, the absolute, the final, the unchanging—and that our knowledge of it reflects both the existence of the spiritual realm and the spark of divinity we all carry within us. Love of such superior knowledge ignites the spark, and the Good becomes part of ourselves. This kind of participation is incomprehensible for those who are blinded by the scientific outlook, yet it alone could be responsible for the evolutionary progress of the species. Men who lead lives believing that the Good means what is good for their earthly happiness and survival will hardly be expected to leave records of human greatness for posterity to emulate. But if men were to lead lives in continual striving for knowledge of the

Good through increasingly discerning love and participation, posterity would have grounds for rejoicing. And what is more, the secular would remain secular, and the sacred, sacred—and all modern concepts of humanism would need to be revised.

That which partakes of the divine is no fit subject for scientific investigation. It is sacred. Neither biologists nor humanists can accept this view, but it is conceivable that biological sophrosyne will one day exercise a directive influence upon human behavior. Until then, experimental biologists will undoubtedly continue, for "man's own good," their misguided researches on human emotions and behavior, often by methods involving so much animal suffering that they are humanly degrading. To love the Good of the spiritual realm is to hear humanism's fundamental tone. And to hear it means being aware that those human attributes we call gentleness and restraint must necessarily play a determining role in human conduct. By our standards, a rhesus monkey is a dull-witted animal without any conception of the Good. Yet it has its own niche in the earthly environment and its own form of *arete*. Modern scientists, with the approbation of modern humanists, are subjecting these animals, in highly artificial environments, to extreme mental torture in the proud delusion that they are thereby doing all in their power to help their fellow men. That these experiments are conducted to attain a knowledge of love makes them not only ludicrous but revealing as well. For in the final analysis they reveal a grave lack of understanding of the subject that is believed to be under investigation.

These words, then, are meant primarily as an appeal to the genuine humanists of our day to join forces to combat the basic beliefs of the pseudo-humanists. Prizing our spiritual heritage more than scientific knowledge, we have nothing to fear. We are on the side of the angels.

Epilogue

ΓΝΩΘΙ ΣΕΑΥΤΟΝ
(Know Thyself)

Let us try to reinforce the master theme of this book by assembling and supplementing the related threads of the preceding chapters. These manifold threads, each bearing upon some aspect of modern biology's relation to humanism, followed readily one upon another; beginning with a critique of the modern scientist's mental outlook, the train of thought expressed in the succeeding pages ended in the conviction that scientism's dehumanizing trends can be extirpated. The master theme can thus be delineated as an attempt to provide, with particular reference to biology, a remedy for the incompatibility between scientific progress and human progress.

Recognition of this incompatibility is inconspicuous in the twentieth-century's *Weltanschauung*, despite its awareness of both the blessings and the dangers of the already existing applications of scientific knowledge. We all appreciate the role science has played in alleviating human disease, want, and suffering. In fact, the constant hope of an ever increasing store of such benefits has been largely responsible for the past four centuries of flourishing scientific activity. Man's thirst for new knowledge is not solely dependent upon his desire to understand the world but also upon his desire to utilize this understanding in the improvement of his lot. Consequently, the contemporary scientist, who provides the knowledge upon which human amelioration depends, is universally respected and esteemed.

At the same time, we are all aware of other kinds of application of scientific knowledge, such as the deliberate production of nuclear weapons, the accidental pollution of the earth and its atmosphere with chemicals, or the unforeseen effects of thalidomide drugs. Denouncing such banes, we nevertheless continue to extol the scientist and his triumphant forward march. Whether scientific advance be experimental, theoretical, or descriptive, and whether it lead ultimately to benefits, evils, or to no application at all, its actual pursuit enjoys the zealous and unstinting support of modern society. In view of the increasing perils of the utilization of scientific knowledge, why does any investigation which can be called "scientific" automatically convince both the scientist and the layman that it is intrinsically valuable for the promotion of human progress? The answer is twofold: it is based upon current ideas concerning (1) the application of scientific knowledge and (2) the motivation of scientific inquiry.

First, of course, is the belief that all of the new practical benefits to be derived from scientific progress will far outweigh the evils. The general outlook of the inhabitants of civilized countries is understandably influenced by the power of science, technology, and medicine to make both life and death easier for them. It is also influenced by the present explosive growth of the world population and the consequent need to supply an increasing number of suffering human beings with what they lack. The rapid advance of science is thus generally held to be not only highly desirable but urgently necessary.

However, the contention that the practical utilization of scientific advance will necessarily lead to far more good than harm is highly dubious. Modern society seems to have no conception of what may be in store if the proposals made by contemporary biologists for utilizing their newly acquired knowledge ever become realities. That these proposals represent the considered judgment of the leaders of the scientific profession is no guarantee that they are humanly desirable. They proclaim, in fact, that the dream of modern biology is to direct the evolution of *Homo sapiens* through its scientifically controlled transformation—surely the most presumptuous and misguided attempt to improve human nature ever conceived. For the means required are first, that science indoctrinate man in the belief that his further evolutionary progress requires a renunciation of his gods in favor of the scientific *Weltbild;* second, that science sanction the physical and mental suffering of countless numbers of experimental animals in its all-out effort to attain more objective knowledge about every aspect of human life; and, finally, that science take direct charge of man's evolution by the genetic, chemical, and perhaps even surgical manipulation of the human body.

A distinguished theoretical physicist has been quoted as saying that the members of his profession are not to blame for the existence of nuclear weapons. I suppose many people today would acquiesce in this contention. But I think that no amount of respect or admiration for scientists could ever be sufficient grounds for exculpating those contemporary biologists who wish to effect the scientific transformation of the human race. Even to suggest such application of scientific knowledge reveals that the amoral objectivity upon which scientists pride themselves has been replaced by an immorality which threatens both themselves and future generations.

From the world at large these evolutionary visions of contemporary biologists have hitherto met little resistance. Presumably they are either unknown or regarded as desirable, inevitable goals. In either case, their dehumanizing significance has penetrated neither man's consciousness nor conscience. Science, recognizing no limitations, has been so tremendously successful in alleviating physical and mental afflictions and in prolonging life that it now seems quite natural that further scientific progress should include the alteration of man's genes, mind, and spirit. Those who would not be so altered may soon be forced to challenge the current idolatry of science.

However, our present enthusiasm for science rests upon more than a desire for a scientifically directed world and a partial blindness to the potential risks associated with the proposed applications of scientific knowledge. A second and, I believe, more important cause for our enthusiasm is based upon our concept of the aims of pure science. The generally accepted view, both within and without scientific and humanistic circles, is that the supreme motivation of scientific inquiry, transcending even the human benefits which may accrue from its application, is our dispassionate and disinterested desire to discover the truth. Man takes so much pride in his uncontrollable curiosity and his scientific objectivity that both are regarded as among the most desirable of human attributes. *Ergo,* the prime duty of a scientist is to advance scientific knowledge to the limit of his intellectual ability. We thus sit back in comfortable assurance that although we may possibly need to concern ourselves with the goals of applied science, the basic motivation of pure science need never be questioned. This assurance is fallacious: the motives and goals of scientific research do need to be questioned.

Eight years ago Michael Polanyi did so, thus pointing the way.[1] With elegant logic and eloquent persuasion he attacked the modern delusion of detached scientific objectivity. Maintaining that scientific knowledge is a union of the objective and the personal, he regarded the continued neglect of the personal element of scientific motivation as both dangerous and immoral. The attainment of scientific knowledge is not, according to Polanyi, detached and impersonal achievement, but rests ultimately upon belief, and failure to recognize this fact only widens the gulf between science and humanism.

In a 1963 commencement address at a medical college in Philadelphia, Barry Commoner, a molecular biologist, also questioned the motives and goals of pure science.[2] Approaching the problem from a different perspective, he did not, however, discuss Polanyi's belief that scientific objectivity could be a delusion. The main theme of his address was rather an attack upon the omnipresent notion that man must necessarily make use of the power science has given him. In developing this theme by referring explicitly to the exploration of space, Commoner went beyond a denial of the inevitability of the application of scientific knowledge: he also questioned the ultimate reasons for scientific research. His critique of the motivation behind the American space research program was at the same time an appeal to reconsider the widespread belief that what man can do, he must do—and it was thereby an appeal to reconsider the basic aims of pure as well as applied science. He wisely pointed out that the reluctance of the Scientific Age to oppose the progress of science is responsible for its failure to consider whether the new scientific knowledge so sought would be humanly desirable. Yet he remained convinced that man's desires will eventually be found to center upon the "still urgent need to secure the life of man on earth" rather than on the advance of "that system of objective, detached, transcending knowledge which is science." In other words, Commoner emphasized the necessity of future scientific progress being responsible primarily to human survival and well-being.

Both Polanyi and Commoner are thus aware of the perils latent in the ultimate aims of modern science. Polanyi stresses how demoralizing it is for the world at large to have scientists mistakenly base their activity upon an impersonal scientific objectivity which does not, in fact, exist; Commoner, although believing that scientific activity is objective, stresses that it must place human needs higher than its own unlimited, and often unnecessary expansion.

The warnings of Polanyi and Commoner can be even further extended: another danger is already emerging out of this flourishing human activity that takes so much pride in its detached devotion to the search for truth. This danger is what Lewis Mumford, in his brilliant probing of the motivation of science and scholarship, has termed the "automation of knowledge."[3] Whether scientists are driven by scientific objectivity, uncontrollable curiosity, intellectual passion, personal commitment, economic interests, fame, recognition, and applause, belief in the necessity of novel applications of science, or an altruistic desire to benefit their fellow men, their personal motives seem to matter very little to the society which supports them—so long as they continue to amass new objective facts. All the manifold motives of scientific activity are now tending to become subordinate to one supreme motive, which has become a pressing world demand: that man's lack of objective knowledge be supplied at the greatest possible speed.

In Mumford's justly condemnatory words, this automation of knowledge has become an end in itself. The world hopes, of course, that the new knowledge attained by scientists will benefit mankind, but even if it doesn't, it must be attained anyway. What man can do, he must do. Like Mallory's mountain, which had to be climbed because it was there, the facts about the universe must, in the same way, be discovered. And why? Because we tacitly assume that the unlimited expansion of the human intellect through the discovery of new objective truths *must* be supremely desirable since it is a predestined part of human evolution: intellectually, man *must* become increasingly whole by the indiscriminate expansion of his knowledge. Such reasoning leads straight to the dogged conviction that scientific progress is synonymous with human evolutionary progress.

My own opinion is that the further advancement of science—and particularly, biology—if it continues to be as automatic, mindless, and heartless as modern scientism demands, will not accelerate human evolutionary progress but retard it. For the biologist's ultimate goal cannot be different from that of any other human being: to realize his human potential. And since neither moral apathy nor the objective and automatic nature of current scientific activity offers much promise in the attainment of this end, let us now consider what other possibilities remain open to him.

When modern biologists contemptuously deny the existing greatness of the species by expressing a desire to alter its spiritual characteristics by their own newly discovered methods, they unwittingly disclose one of the most pernicious dogmas of modern scientism—that intelligence is more humanly significant than virtue. Through all its ramifications and extensions, this dogma has led to the present super-organization of scientific activity, to explosive university expansion, to the automation of knowledge, and to the blind desire for an ever increasing "noosphere." The dogma itself remains as the tacit superior knowledge of our day to which we so willingly subscribe; triumphant, powerful, and recognizing no limitations, it insists upon an unrestricted and all-out scientific attack upon all aspects of life.

This is not to neglect those biologists who have given thought to the limitations of their activity. Besides Commoner's warnings and those of Sirks[4] and Eiseley[5] referred to in the first chapter, we have, for example, from the field of zoology, the highly interesting reflections of Adolphe Portmann concerning the relation of biology to the realm of the spiritual, which he recognized in animals as well as man and which he associated with the limits of scientific research. The outer appearance of animals, according to Portmann, reflects their "inwardness," and the fact that this self-representation can often be unrelated to utility or survival "indicates the limit of interpretation by biological method. . . . Order at this limit . . . brings us to realms with which the word 'spirit,' in one of its meanings, is often associated."[6] "Life," he writes elsewhere, "is always more than science can say about it at any given time."[7]

These voices of the unorthodox have had very little influence in stemming the tide. It is, however, conceivable that our descendants may witness the self-limitation of biological research as we know it today. Modern biology is concerned with the objective, scientific study of the organisms, organs, tissues, cells, and subcellular units of which all life is composed, and no one can deny that such an activity is valuable. But it is of limited value for the survival or the progress of the species, both of which depend, in the final analysis, upon man's awareness of the realm of the spirit.

Science is a recent human activity, and having deliberately renounced as much subjective judgment as possible in order to proceed, it has at the same time divorced itself from the age-old problems of morality. This renunciation renders science, even when it takes man as the object of its investigations, incapable of adding to our knowledge of man's uniqueness: his awareness of the good. Nor can scientific knowledge about animals—that knowledge which Aldous Huxley desired in order to make us more whole—teach us anything about this essence of our uniqueness, from which all animal life is necessarily excluded. The same holds true of scientific investigations of all other forms of life. Why, then, all this compulsive, reckless, and unrestricted advance of biology into every part of the organic world? And why does it so often proceed, as in the rhesus experiments, with a complete lack of veneration and compassion for living things?

A biologist of the future who cared to ask himself these questions would probably pursue his activity with more humility, restraint, and moderation than does a contemporary biologist who ignores them. Respect for all forms of life may one day be proportional to the zoologist's or the botanist's proximity to the spiritual realm. By the same token, man's desire to study himself will, I think, be redirected into new approaches through the realization that scientific activity as we know it today cannot augment human virtue. Present-day geneticists, physiologists, psychologists, and psychoanalysts would no doubt disagree with this contention. Yet the fact remains that a scientific explanation of virtue is an impossibility—and their own professional activities are the result of scientific education rather than preoccupation with morality and religion. When biologists begin to study man by first of all centering their attention upon the past realizations of his spiritual greatness, the now fashionable proposals to "improve" him by scientific methods will appear in their true light—as the groping, misguided visions of the early stages of biology. Biologists of the future may find it necessary to impose limits on their own activity for the sake of their own potential.

Here, the ideas of Polanyi are relevant. It will be remembered he declared that the most important scientific visions of reality—those which partake of universal significance—are attainable only when the scientist is aware of his own intellectual passions and his personal commitment to the truth. However, the biological visions of reality that are now being attained are dehumanizing and demoralizing in the extreme. It appears, then, that something more than passion and commitment is required of a biologist if he is to attain a universally significant vision. I believe that Polanyi himself supplied the answer by anticipating the eventual extension of biology into what he called "ultra-biology." Here the biologist who wished to comprehend life would necessarily center his attention upon forms of life higher than himself—upon human life at its greatest. And in doing so, he would be forced to recognize the folly of trying to understand and control life by the methods and aims of twentieth-century biology. For a knowledge of the greatness of human life is attainable only by the commitment and participation of those who passionately desire spiritual improvement. Human *arete*, springing from the human-divine interrelation, cannot be comprehended by contemporary scientific investigation. Its comprehension requires moral aspiration.

This, admittedly, is to identify future human evolution with moral progress, but I believe that the Scientific Age will be required to accept this point of view. Those who are now unprepared to do so will regard it as merely a vague, unrealistic hope of somehow "humanizing" the scientist—and that in only one particular direction. Reason alone, they might insist, should at once deter anyone from a dogmatic attempt to consider knowledge of the Good as the highest kind of superior knowledge, thereby elevating it above those two other kinds of knowledge, Truth and Beauty. Is not their attainment, in the form of science and art, of equal significance for human progress? To deal fully with this problem would lead to a discussion of the human psyche and the interrelations of the unconscious and the conscious, the sexual and the spiritual, and motives and free will—all of which lie far beyond the scope of this book and the competence of its author.

Suffice it to say that since Socrates, the human species has been blessed with the idea that each individual, if he so chooses, can regard the attainment of knowledge as active participation rather than passive reception. This idea, with its connotation of self-improvement, is, I believe, of supreme evolutionary significance. In considering now the kinds of knowledge that are most conducive to self-improvement, it appears that although truth, beauty, and goodness are interrelated in some way which we cannot wholly grasp, participation in truth and beauty seems to need an ethical directive for its fullest realization. In considering, for example, participation in modern scientific truth, one is reminded of these words of Charles Davy: "The difference between acquiring knowledge in the present and the past was that formerly it could be acquired only by someone changing himself. Today, anyone with the necessary ability can acquire it."[8] It is certainly true that the objective knowledge acquired through modern education is for the most part passive reception and the dissemination itself is likewise of a predominantly passive character. Further, participation in the organization, teamwork, and efficiency of modern scientific research makes it rare indeed for a scientist to become basically altered by the acquisition of a new scientific truth. I am not forgetting his possible intellectual passion for it nor the beauty he may see in it; I am merely stressing the fact that the modern scientist's participation in his activity is for the most part centered upon the desire to discover new truths, not upon the desire for self-improvement. And with respect to aesthetic participation in the various forms of art, everyone is aware how intensely interesting, enjoyable, and satisfying it can be. Yet I believe that in some ineffable way a human soul exposed to a Mozart string quintet is elevated in proportion to its attempt to approximate this experience to the moral values of the spiritual world. To be convinced of this need for ethical directives is to believe, with Socrates, that knowledge of the Good is transcendent superior knowledge. And since what man regards as transcendent must be most valuable to him, it follows that this knowledge must be the most basic of all human needs.

The relevance of this line of argument to the need for ethics in our Scientific Age above and beyond its function as a bulwark against the evils of scientific application may now become more clear. Polanyi has justly said that "whenever the current scientific outlook bears directly upon man and society, it affects our world view, and in doing so, tends to render all things meaningless."[9] The dominating influence of the amoral character of modern scientific activity is to a large extent responsible for much of the impermanency, nihilism, and absurdity which permeate our contemporary art, philosophy, and way of life. The twentieth century believes that human progress is exclusively dynamic and is therefore solely dependent upon a continually changing understanding of reality. This is to believe that a quantitative expansion of our knowledge, coupled with ever changing concepts of morality to fit it, is our greatest need. This is also to neglect utterly the enduring efforts of all those before us, who, without any scientific knowledge whatsoever, understood reality so deeply that their realized potentials elevated the essence of the species to which they belonged.

The life and thoughts of a Plato, a Socrates, a Boethius, or a Petrarch are enduring because they reveal the heights which human *arete* can attain. In doing so, they constitute knowledge of how far we have come, of what it means to be a human being. We, their progeny, need to embrace and assimilate this superior knowledge they have given us through our minds and our hearts together. From an evolutionary point of view, nothing less will suffice. For such knowledge also represents a part of the unrealized potential of the species, whose further ascent depends upon its knowing how much "goodness" it possesses. Now, in the psychosocial stage of human evolution, with all of its possibilities for cultural contact and transmission, the species appears at last to possess the means of realizing this part of its potential through the active participation of its individual members.

These concluding words are primarily addressed to the modern biologist, yet, in a sense, they also apply to those engaged in any other field of science—for in embracing the whole vision of "ultra-biology," they necessarily touch upon the essential humanness of each one of us. And with this thought, it seems that we now approach the heart of the matter.

I suggest, therefore, that a possible remedy for the present incompatibility between scientific progress and human progress is that the scientist recognize the evolutionary significance of his only standard of humanness and act accordingly. This would mean an awareness, awakened by love, of human *arete* as the most precious knowledge, and the concomitant desire to participate in it.

Such personal participation in this kind of superior knowledge should have far-reaching consequences for further scientific progress. In the first place, since scientists would be forced to center their attention upon the qualitative expansion of knowledge, the precipitate advance of science would be retarded, restricted, and redirected—for the benefit of all concerned. At the same time, a gradual reconciliation between the objective and the subjective world outlooks could be envisaged, since both scientists and the society that supports them would necessarily recognize the dangers inherent in a single outlook which overemphasized the objective, the material, and the intellectual, as well as the quantitative, the novel, and the amoral. And, finally, such participation should effectively arrest the dehumanizing trends that now prevail in nearly all fields of science, but which are most flagrant in the biological sciences. For we must not forget that the modern biologist, basing his wisdom on the last four hundred years—6 percent of man's civilized life—evaluates scientific knowledge so highly that he now wishes to hasten his evolution by utilizing it in his self-transformation. If, instead, he would look further back to those ideas of self-transformation through participation in the spiritual realm, he might choose as the key to his evolution the realized potentials of the human spirit. For it is by such knowledge we are defined, now and forever.

Let no one, however, minimize the dangers involved in attempting to augment one's humanness by participating in the highest form of superior knowledge. Not only can one's motives and intentions be misunderstood and challenged, but one's balance and perspective can be distorted by the damaging inflation of the ego and by both body and soul becoming possessed by the vision. At every step errors of judgment with tragic or disastrous consequences threaten him who believes himself committed to choose from life that which will best nourish his soul. Yet it is through such repeated attempts to participate in the highest manifestations of the human spirit that we can understand the human-divine interrelation and teach our descendants to love in the fullness of their hearts the *arete* of *Homo sapiens*. For those who teach must also know—intellectually and emotionally—the greatness of the potential each one of us already has within himself.

Only by first realizing the individual human potentials of its members can the species as a whole be elevated. Only by such self-knowledge can it hope in the fullness of time to surpass itself. This is humanism. Is it not the prime stuff of biology as well?

References

Chapter I

1. M. J. Sirks, "L'homme considéré comme objet de la biologie," *Folia Biotheoretica* (1960), vol. 5, p. 58.
2. W. Weaver, *A Great Age for Science,* pamphlet of the Alfred P. Sloan Foundation (New York, 1960).
3. Arnold J. Toynbee, *Hellenism, the History of a Civilization* (New York, 1959).
4. Werner Jaeger, *Paideia: The Ideals of Greek Culture,* vol. I (New York, 1945).
5. Gilbert Murray, *The Rise of the Greek Epic* (London, 1934).
6. P. Teilhard de Chardin, *The Phenomenon of Man* (New York, 1959).
7. Barry Commoner, "In Defense of Biology," *Science* (1961), vol. 133, p. 1745.
8. Gilbert Murray, *op. cit.*
9. Albert Schweitzer, *The Philosophy of Civilization* (London, 1923, 1946).
10. Loren Eiseley, *The Immense Journey* (New York, 1957).
11. Benjamin Farrington, "Science and the Classics," *Nature* (1961), vol. 191, p. 1337.

12. Lewis Mumford, *The Conduct of Life* (New York, 1951).

Chapter II

1. Julian Huxley, "Eugenics in Evolutionary Perspective," *Perspectives in Biology and Medicine* (1963), vol. 6, p. 155.
2. P. Teilhard de Chardin, *The Phenomenon of Man, op. cit.*
3. W. Heitler, "Ethik des naturwissenschaftlichen Zeitalters," *Universitas* (1964), vol. 19, p. 621.
4. Lewis Mumford, *The Conduct of Life* and also *The Transformations of Man* (London, 1957).
5. Julian Huxley, "Eugenics in Evolutionary Perspective," *op. cit.*
6. *Ibid.*
7. *Ibid.*
8. Werner Jaeger, *Paideia: The Ideals of Greek Culture*, vol. II (New York, 1943).
9. Julian Huxley, in *Evolution and Ethics, 1893-1943* (London, 1947).

Chapter III

1. William H. Prescott, *History of the Conquest of Mexico and the Conquest of Peru* (New York, n.d.).
2. C. Singer, *A Short History of Biology* (Oxford, 1931).
3. W. R. Inge, *Christian Ethics and Modern Problems* (London, 1930).
4. E. D. Weitzman and G. S. Ross, "A Behavioral Method for the Study of Pain Perception in the Monkey," *Neurology* (1962), vol. 12, p. 264.
5. M. I. Gregersen and W. S. Root, "Experimental Traumatic Shock Produced by Muscle Contusion with a Note on the Effects of Bullet Wounds," *American Journal of Physiology* (1947), vol. 148, p. 98.
6. D. J. Ingle, "The Care and Treatment of Animals," *Perspectives in Biology and Medicine* (1963), vol. 6, p. 256, and also "Letters from the Editor," *op. cit.* (1963), vol. 7, p. 132.
7. J. Börtz, "De smertevoldende Dyreforsøg," *Forsøgsdyrenes Vaern* (1963), vol. 1, no. 3, p. 3.
8. A. Garboe, "Den nye Forening," *Forsøgsdyrenes Vaern* (1963), vol. 1, no. 1, p. 1.
9. D. J. Ingle, "The Care and Treatment of Animals," *op. cit.*
10. D. J. Ingle, "Letters from the Editor," *op. cit.*
11. Charles Davy, *Towards a Third Culture* (London, 1961).

Chapter IV

1. Michael Polanyi, *Personal Knowledge. Towards a Post-Critical Philosophy* (Chicago, 1958).
2. Michael Polanyi, "Scientific Outlook: Its Sickness and Cure," *Science* (1957), vol. 125, p. 480.
3. Julian Huxley, "Eugenics in Evolutionary Perspective," *op. cit.*
4. P. Teilhard de Chardin, *The Phenomenon of Man, op. cit.*
5. Michael Polanyi, *Personal Knowledge* and also "Scientific Outlook: Its Sickness and Cure," *op. cit.*
6. Lewis Mumford, "Anticipations and Social Consequences of Atomic Energy," *American Philosophical Society Proceedings* (1954), vol. 98, p. 149.
7. Loren Eiseley, *The Immense Journey* and also *The Firmament of Time* (London, 1961).
8. F. M. R. Walshe, "Some Views upon the Nature of the Relationship between Mind and Brain," *Journal of Medical Education* (1959), vol. 34, p. 1110.
9. Benjamin Farrington, "Science and the Classics," *op. cit.*
10. W. Heitler, "Ethik des naturwissenschaftlichen Zeitalters," *op. cit.*, and also "Die Wirkung des naturwissenschaftlichen Denkens auf den Menschen," *Arbeitstagung der Gesellschaft zur Förderung der wissenschaftlichen Graphologie* (1963).
11. Rachel Carson, *Silent Spring* (Boston, 1962).
12. Lewis Mumford, "The Automation of Knowledge," address given at the 19th National Conference of Higher Education (Chicago, April 19, 1964).
13. D. J. de S. Price, in *Man and His Future* (London, 1963).
14. Aldous Huxley, *Literature and Science* (New York, 1963).
15. J. Lederberg, "Biological Future of Man," in *Man and His Future.*
16. Lewis Mumford, "The Automation of Knowledge."

Chapter V

1. C. P. Snow, *The Two Cultures: And a Second Look* (Cambridge, 1964).
2. Lewis Mumford, *The Golden Day* (New York, 1926).
3. Charles Davy, *Towards a Third Culture.*
4. M. Yudkin, "Sir Charles Snow's Rede Lecture" in F. R. Leavis, *Two Cultures? The Significance of C. P. Snow* (London, 1962).
5. C. Madge, article in the *Times Literary Supplement* (London, October 25, 1963).
6. Aldous Huxley, *Literature and Science.*
7. Aldous Huxley, *Brave New World Revisited* (New York, 1958).

8. P. Teilhard de Chardin, *The Phenomenon of Man.*
9. Aldous Huxley, *Literature and Science.*
10. Loren Eiseley, *The Immense Journey.*
11. Aldous Huxley, *Literature and Science.*
12. Michael Polanyi, *Personal Knowledge.*
13. Benjamin Farrington, in personal correspondence with the author in 1963.
14. Lewis Mumford, "The Automation of Knowledge."
15. Aldous Huxley, *Literature and Science.*

Chapter VI

1. Morris Bishop, *Petrarch and His World* (Bloomington, Ind., 1963).
2. Benjamin Farrington, "Science and the Classics," *op. cit.*
3. J. A. Symonds, article on the Renaissance in *Encyclopedia Britannica*, 13th ed. (1926).
4. Julian Huxley, *Essays of a Humanist* (New York, 1964).
5. Moses Hadas, *Humanism* (New York, 1960).
6. J. Lawrence in *The Honest to God Debate* (London, 1963).
7. Ronald Hepburn, "A Critique of Humanist Theology," *Objections to Humanism* (London, 1963).
8. H. Hawton, *The Humanist Revolution* (London, 1963).
9. H. J. Blackman, "Humanism: The Subject of the Objections," *Objections to Humanism.*
10. H. Hawton, *op. cit.*
11. H. F. Harlow, "The Nature of Love," *American Psychologist* (1958), vol. 13, p. 673.
12. H. F. Harlow, "Love in Infant Monkeys," *Scientific American* (1959), vol. 200, p. 68.
13. H. F. and M. K. Harlow, "Social Deprivation in Monkeys," *Scientific American* (1962), vol. 207, p. 136.
14. H. F. Harlow, "Love in Infant Monkeys," *op. cit.*
15. G. Møller, "Harlow's Primatforsøg i psykologisk og ethologisk Belysning," *Naturens Verden* (October, 1965), p. 298.
16. Julian Huxley, *Essays of a Humanist.*
17. E. and W. Menaker, *Ego in Evolution* (New York, 1965).
18. J. A. T. Robinson in *Honest to God* (London, 1963).
19. Julian Huxley, *Essays of a Humanist.*
20. M. L. Smith, "The World Without God," *The Humanist* (1965), vol. 80, p. 305.
21. H. Hawton, *op. cit.*
22. E. and W. Menaker, *Ego in Evolution*, and also Julian Huxley, *Essays of a Humanist.*

23. Julian Huxley, *Essays of a Humanist.*
24. M. M. Hunt, "Love in a Humanist Frame," in *The Humanist Frame* (London, 1961).
25. Charles Davy, *Towards a Third Culture.*

Epilogue

1. Michael Polanyi, *Personal Knowledge.*
2. Barry Commoner, "The Responsibility of Science to Man," *Perspectives in Biology and Medicine* (1964), vol. 8, p. 85.
3. Lewis Mumford, "The Automation of Knowledge."
4. M. J. Sirks, "L'homme considéré comme objet de la biologie," *op. cit.*
5. Loren Eiseley, *The Immense Journey.*
6. Adolphe Portmann, "Biology and the Phenomenon of the Spiritual," in *Spirit and Nature* (New York, 1954).
7. Adolphe Portmann, *New Paths in Biology* (New York, 1964).
8. Charles Davy, *Towards a Third Culture.*
9. Michael Polanyi, "Science and Man's Place in the Universe," in *Science as a Cultural Force* (Baltimore, 1964).

Index